Short Plays 1

Roberta Koch Suid
James Higgins
Murray Suid

James Moffett, Senior Editor

Houghton Mifflin Company • Boston

Atlanta   Dallas   Geneva, Illinois   Hopewell, New Jersey   Palo Alto

Copyright © 1973 by Houghton Mifflin Company. All rights reserved. No part of this work may be reproduced or transmitted in any form or by any means, electronic or mechanical, including photocopying and recording, or by any information storage or retrieval system, without permission in writing from the publisher. Printed in the U.S.A.

The Heroic Vegetables — A Puppet Play, copyright © 1973 by James Higgins and Murray Suid.

A Spider Spectacular, copyright © 1973 by Rod Coneybeare.

Wizard of Oz, still #1060-50, 132, 133, 8, 206. © 1939, Metro-Goldwyn-Mayer Inc.

ISBN: 0-395-13824-8

Acknowledgments

Plays, Inc., Publishers for *The King's Bean Soup* by Sally Werner. Reprinted from *Children's Plays from Favorite Stories*. Edited by Sylvia E. Kamerman, Plays, Inc., Publishers, Boston, Mass., 02116. Copyright © 1954 by Plays, Inc. For *African Trio* by Barbara Winther. Reprinted from *Dramatized Folk Tales of the World*. Edited by Sylvia E. Kamerman. Plays, Inc., Publishers, Boston, Mass., 02116. Copyright © 1969 by Plays, Inc. For *The Wizard of Oz*, adapted by Lynne Sharon Schwartz. Reprinted from *Fifty Plays for Junior Actors*. Edited by Sylvia E. Kamerman. Plays, Inc., Publishers, Boston, Mass., 02116. Copyright © 1963 by Plays, Inc.

Harper & Row, Publishers, Inc., for *How Boots Befooled the King* from *Wonder Clock Plays*, adapted from Howard Pyle's *The Wonder Clock* by Sophie L. Goldsmith. Copyright, 1925, by Harper & Brothers; renewed, 1953, by Sophie L. Goldsmith.

Contents

Next, see "Stage a Play" and "You're on the Air" in DOING; "Doing
Pantomime," "Story Theater," "Making a Play," and "Be an Actor"
in ACTING OUT.

Plays on circled ○ pages have been recorded. Look for them under
Short Plays 1 in the LISTENING LIBRARY.

The King's Bean Soup

by Sally Werner

Characters

KING
FOUR ATTENDANTS
COURT JESTER
PALACE COOK
THREE COOKS
PAGE
BEGGAR

SETTING: *Throne room of the King's palace*
AT RISE: *The four* ATTENDANTS *are pacing back and forth across the stage.*

1ST ATTENDANT: The King has lost his appetite. He refuses everything. He wants nothing but bean soup.

2ND ATTENDANT: If it were only as simple as that. It must be a special kind of bean soup — an old fashioned kind of bean soup.

Reprinted from *Children's Plays from Favorite Stories*, edited by Sylvia E. Kamerman, Plays, Inc., Publishers, Boston, Mass. 02116. Copyright © 1954 by Plays, Inc.

1

3RD ATTENDANT: Made from an old recipe his great-grand-mother, the Queen of the North Country, once had.

4TH ATTENDANT: We have searched through all the cook-books in the palace. We have tried all the recipes for bean soup. His Majesty insists that we have not found the right recipe.

1ST ATTENDANT: Oh, dear, something must be done. The King must have his bean soup. He has scarcely eaten anything for a week.

PAGE (*Rushing in*): The cook has found it! He has found the lost recipe for bean soup!

1ST ATTENDANT (*To* 2ND ATTENDANT): They have found the recipe.

2ND ATTENDANT (*To* 3RD ATTENDANT): They have found the recipe.

3RD ATTENDANT (*To* 4TH ATTENDANT): They have found the recipe.

ALL: They have found the recipe! The King shall have his bean soup!

JESTER (*Comes in dancing and singing*): Bean soup! Bean soup! The King shall have his bean soup! (*Dances out again*)

PALACE COOK (*Comes in carrying old cookbook*): Alas and alas! The recipe is old and torn. One ingredient is missing.

1ST ATTENDANT: Ssh! Not so loud. The King must not know. Prepare the soup anyway. Perhaps he will not notice. Make haste! (COOK *hurries away.*)

4TH ATTENDANT: Meanwhile, we must try to find the miss-ing ingredient. I will send word to all the best cooks in the land. Surely someone will know what is missing.

2

ALL: Yes — yes. Make haste. (4TH ATTENDANT *hurries away as* KING *enters and sits on throne.* ATTENDANTS *bow.*)

KING (*Shakes head sadly*): Oh, I feel weak — I feel faint. Oh, that I could have but one sip of my favorite bean soup.

1ST ATTENDANT: We have good news, your Majesty.

2ND ATTENDANT: Very good news, your Majesty.

3RD ATTENDANT: Excellent news, your Majesty.

1ST ATTENDANT: The lost recipe has been found.

KING (*Very excited*): You mean my great-grandmother's bean soup recipe?

2ND ATTENDANT: Yes, your Majesty. The recipe has been found.

KING: And I am to have my bean soup today?

ALL (*Bowing*): Yes, your Majesty — today.

KING: Ah! At last! At last! My favorite bean soup. Ah! (PALACE COOK *enters, carrying bowl and spoon on tray. Places it before* KING. *He tastes it, smacks, rolls eyes upward, frowns, shakes head.*) No — no — no! Something is missing. It is not the same, I tell you. It lacks something. Why, oh why, can't I have my favorite bean soup? (*Puts head in hands and groans*) Take this soup out and give it to the beggars at the roadside. Take it away! (PALACE COOK *takes tray and leaves.* 2ND ATTENDANT *accompanies him.*)

1ST ATTENDANT: Your Majesty, let me explain. The recipe was found at last, but it was in a very old book and one ingredient was torn away. We thought it was some small item of little importance, so the soup was made anyway.

4

KING: The missing ingredient must be found I tell you! It must be found! Why don't you do something?

3RD ATTENDANT: We — we have, your Majesty. We have sent word to all the best cooks in the land. They should be here very soon and someone will know what is missing from the recipe.

KING: Whoever finds the missing ingredient shall be well rewarded.

4TH ATTENDANT (*Entering and bowing before* KING): The very best cooks in the land have come, your Majesty. First comes the cook from the Hill Country.

1ST COOK (*Enters carrying bowl of soup on tray*): Your Highness, I have prepared bean soup from the lost recipe and added a very special herb which grows only in the Hill Country. I am the only one who knows about this herb, sire, and I believe it is the missing ingredient. (KING *tastes soup, frowns, and shakes head.*)

KING: Take it away! That is not the bean soup I am longing for. You have not found the missing ingredient. (1ST COOK *takes tray and leaves.*)

4TH ATTENDANT: The very best cook from the Low Country is here, your Majesty.

2ND COOK (*Enters, carrying bowl of soup*): Your Highness, I have prepared bean soup from the lost recipe and added a very special herb which grows only in the Low Country. I am the only one who knows about this herb, sire. I am sure it must be the missing ingredient. (KING *tastes soup, frowns, and shakes head.*)

KING: Take it away! That is not the missing ingredient. (2ND COOK *takes tray and leaves.*) Why, oh why, can't I have my favorite bean soup?

4TH ATTENDANT: Your Highness, the very best cook from the Island Country is here.

3RD COOK (*Enters, carrying bowl of soup on tray*): Your Highness, I have prepared bean soup from the lost recipe and added a special plant which grows only at the bottom of the sea. Only I know about this plant and I am sure it is the missing ingredient, sire. (KING *tastes soup, frowns, and shakes head.*)

KING: No — *no* — *no!* This is not right. (*Gives bowl back.* COOK *leaves.*) Is there no one in the world who knows what the missing ingredient might be? Why, oh why, can't I have my favorite bean soup? Oh, that my royal great-grandmother were here. Only she would know what is missing. (*There is a great noise offstage and* 2ND ATTENDANT *comes in dragging a ragged* BEGGAR *who carries a pot of soup.*) What is this great commotion?

2ND ATTENDANT: We found this beggar, your Majesty, begging for food on the palace grounds. That is quite against the rules, sire.

KING: Did you not give him the bean soup my cook prepared?

2ND ATTENDANT: We did, your Majesty, but he will not go away. He says he wishes to talk to the King. What shall we do with him, sire?

KING: Beggar, what have you to say for yourself?

BEGGAR (*Bowing in front of* KING): Your Majesty, they said they brought me bean soup. I think you should know, your Highness, that there is one ingredient missing.

6

KING (*Jumps up*): And do you know what that ingredient might be? What is wrong with this bean soup they keep bringing me? Speak up, beggar.

BEGGAR: They have forgotten to add the beans, sire.

ALL (*Repeating one after the other*): No beans? No beans?

BEGGAR: Your Majesty, may I add that the soup is made from a very old and very tasty recipe. I have added the beans and I would feel greatly honored to have your Majesty taste the soup now.

KING: Indeed I will. Here — let me try it. (BEGGAR *comes forward and bows.* KING *tastes soup, rolls eyes, smacks his lips and then smiles.*)

KING: Ah-h-h!

ALL: Ah-h-h!

KING: My great-grandmother's bean soup! This is it! This is it! Beggar, you shall be well rewarded. You have found the missing ingredient. What is your wish?

BEGGAR: My wish?

KING: Yes, beggar. You shall be my royal cook. You shall have fine clothes and gold and you shall ride in a fine chariot. You shall be very happy. (BEGGAR *looks sad.*) What is the trouble, beggar?

BEGGAR: Your Majesty, you are much too kind. I cannot accept.

KING: Nonsense! I insist!

BEGGAR: I couldn't think of it, your Majesty.

KING: Don't be silly. It's all settled.

BEGGAR: But, your Majesty — the only thing I can cook is bean soup.

KING (*A little worried*): Only bean soup?

8

BEGGAR (*Nodding*): Only bean soup.

KING: Hmm. That means we would have to eat bean soup every day. (BEGGAR *nods.* KING *shakes his head, then smiles.*) I have it! You shall be royal cook for Saturdays. Every Saturday you shall come to the palace and make bean soup for me.

BEGGAR: I would be happy to do that, your Majesty. (*He bows low.*)

JESTER (*Dancing about and singing as the curtains close*): Saturday, bean soup — all you lucky people, I wish the same to you.

The End

The Heroic Vegetables

A Puppet Play
by Murray Suid and James Higgins

Characters

LULA, *a young girl*	SQUASH
LUCKY, *a young boy*	POTATO
TOMATO	CELERY
CARROT	ONION
CORN	RADISH
LETTUCE	CHORUS OF VEGETABLES
PEAS	AND FRUITS
STRINGBEAN	GIANT
BEET	BANANA

SCENE 1

SETTING: *Outside of Lucky's home early one summer morning*

LULA (*Cheerful*): Good morning, Lucky.

LUCKY (*Bored*): Oh, hum.

LULA: What's wrong with you? It's a beautiful morning. The sun is shining and the birds are singing. You're frowning as if it were the end of the world.

LUCKY: It might as well be. There's nothing to do around here.

LULA: How can you say that? We can go swimming or bike riding. Or we can find our friends and have running races. There's lots we can do.

10

LUCKY: Aw, that's the regular stuff. I'd like to do something different.

LULA: Like what?

LUCKY: I don't know. Something exciting.

LULA: You mean like rescuing someone from a giant?

LUCKY: That's exactly what I meant. I'd like to go and rescue somebody from the mean old giant who lives up on Scariest Hill.

LULA: I didn't know there was a giant up there.

LUCKY: Of course there is; only people don't talk about him because they're afraid of him.

LULA: Has he captured anybody yet?

LUCKY: Nobody I know of.

LULA: Then how are you going to rescue somebody if the giant hasn't captured anybody?

LUCKY: That's a good question. I'll have to ask the giant about it when I see him.

LULA: Well, take me along with you. I'll bet the mean old giant will capture me since I'm so pretty. Then you can rescue me.

LUCKY (*Uncertain*): That's a great idea, Lula. But I still don't think I'll take you with me. It might be very dangerous.

LULA (*Stamping her foot*): You have to take me. The whole thing was my idea and if you won't take me, I won't let you use my idea.

LUCKY: O.K., then. Come on. Let's hurry. We can take a shortcut through Mr. Farmer's vegetable garden. (*Sound of footsteps*)

SCENE 2

SETTING: *Mr. Farmer's vegetable garden. The various vegetables are standing around, enjoying the sun.*

LULA: This *is* exciting. We'll get that mean old giant.

TOMATO (*Loud female voice*): You'd better watch your step!

LULA: What did you say, Lucky?

LUCKY: I didn't say anything.

LULA: Somebody said something.

TOMATO: I did.

LUCKY (*Surprised*): But you're a tomato. Tomatoes can't talk.

TOMATO: Really? Then what do you think I'm doing?

LUCKY: Talking, I guess.

TOMATO: Ha!

LUCKY: Well, maybe you're not a tomato.

TOMATO (*Annoyed*): Oh, come on. What do I look like?

LUCKY: You're very red and round with a little green stem.

TOMATO; So?

LUCKY: I have to admit you *do* look like a tomato.

TOMATO: Of course I'm a tomato. A talking tomato, as you can plainly see and hear.

LULA: Since when can tomatoes talk?

TOMATO: Since always. Most people would never think of talking to us, though, so most of the time we don't talk to people.

LULA: Well, hello, Tomato. My name is Lula. This is my friend Lucky.

TOMATO: Hi, Lula. Hi, Lucky. Meet my friends Lettuce, Carrot, Corn, and all the other vegetables. And I'd like you to meet Banana with a few of his friends.

CHORUS OF VEGETABLES AND FRUITS: Hi, Lucky and Lula.

LUCKY and LULA: Hi. Nice to meet you all.

CARROT (*Whispering voice*): Are you really off to challenge the giant?

LUCKY: Yes, we are, Carrot.

CORN (*Giggling voice*): Take us along. It sounds like fun.

LUCKY: We can't take you along. It might be dangerous.

13

TOMATO: Suppose you get hungry on the way?

LULA: We won't be too far from home and plan to be back by lunch.

LETTUCE (*Deep male voice*): *Let us* come. You never know when vegetables can come in handy.

PEAS (*Soft little voice*): Please let us *peas* come.

STRINGBEAN (*Natural voice*): Please let us *string* along.

LUCKY: I don't see how vegetables can help us with the giant.

HEAD OF LETTUCE: Two *heads* are better than one.

LULA: We already have two heads, Lucky's and mine.

LETTUCE: Three heads are better than two.

CARROT: And I can help you get there faster because I have the best *route*.

LUCKY: Route? Oh, *root*. I get it.

CORN: Ha! Ha! That's pretty *corny*.

CARROT: Look who's talking.

BEET (*Deep male voice*): Don't forget me. If there's a fight, I can help you *beat* the giant.

FRUITS (*Pleading voice*): How about us? We'd like to come, too!

LUCKY: O.K. Enough of this. We might as well take all of you vegetables and your friends along.

CHORUS OF VEGETABLES AND FRUITS (*Loud cheering*): Hurrah!

LUCKY: Come on, now. We've got to hurry. Everyone into this big sack. (*Sounds of moaning and groaning*)

LULA: They all fit in there, Lucky. As Lettuce would say, "*Let us go.*"

BEET: Hey! Whoever's on top of me, please move over. You're *squashing* me.

LUCKY: I'll bet I know who's *squashing* Beet.

SQUASH (*Sad voice*): I didn't do anything.

LULA: Oh, boy! (*Sound of footsteps*)

SCENE 3

SETTING: *On top of a hill, in front of the giant's castle*

EVERYBODY: O-O-O! Ah! Wow!

LULA: There's the mean old giant's castle. It's enormous. Maybe we should come back tomorrow. (*Fearfully*)

LUCKY: I told you it would be dangerous. But we're not going back empty handed. Not after I've climbed that hill with this load on my back. And, oh, my back! (*Groans*)

LULA: Put the sack down and rest for a minute.

LUCKY: Whew! O.K. Everyone out of the sack now!

POTATO: Wow! Look at that place. Oh, my, I can see the giant through that open window. He's pacing back and forth.

LULA: You've got a good *eye*, Potato. I wish we could hear what he's saying.

LUCKY: Celery, why don't you *stalk* up there. Take Corn with you. He's got a good *ear*.

SCENE 4

CELERY (*Whispering*): We're back.

LULA (*Whispering*): What did you find out, Celery?

CELERY (*Whispering*): The giant is in there, all right, and is he ever angry. His jester forgot how to make jokes and the giant is sad because he isn't laughing.

LUCKY: That makes sense.

CORN: Not only that. The giant said he would give a big pot of gold to anyone who could make him laugh. And that's why you're lucky.

LUCKY: I'm always Lucky, but why am I lucky now?

16

CORN: The giant wants to laugh, right? And I know plenty of *corny* jokes which will make him laugh.

LULA: Great! Let's all go up there and win that pot of gold. (*Sound of running footsteps*)

SCENE 5

SETTING: *In front of the giant's castle*

LUCKY (*Knocks on the door*): Open up in the name of laughter.

GIANT (*Loud* GIANT'S *voice*): Fe, fi, fo, fum, I smell apples, oranges, tomatoes and a plum. And a boy and a girl.

LUCKY: That's right, Giant. It's me, Lucky, and my friend Lula, and our friends the vegetables and fruits.

GIANT (*Annoyed*): What do you want?

LULA: We've come to win that pot of gold. We can make you laugh.

GIANT: Enter, then. But beware! If you don't make me laugh, I might make you cry.

LUCKY: O.K., Corn. Do your stuff.

CORN (*Giggling voice*): Ready, Giant. Here's a good one. Why did the chicken cross the road?

GIANT: I don't know. Why did the chicken cross the road?

CORN: To get to the other side.

GIANT: Oh, ho! That's funny. Ha, ha!

LUCKY (*Whispers to* LULA): I think that's *corny*.

LULA (*Whispers to* LUCKY): Who cares, if the giant laughs at it.

CORN: Here's another one. Why did the moron tiptoe past the medicine chest?

GIANT: I don't know. Ho, ho. Why did he?

CORN: He didn't want to wake up the sleeping pills.

GIANT (*Laughing very hard*): Ahahahaha! Very funny.

LUCKY: May we have our gold now?

GIANT: Not just yet. I'd like to have all of you for lunch first.

LULA (*Whispers to* LUCKY): I don't like the sound of that.

LUCKY (*Out loud*): I don't think we can stay, Giant. But thank you for inviting us.

GIANT: Oh, but you *must* stay.

LULA: Look out! He's coming after us.

LETTUCE: Onion, help us.

GIANT: I've got you, Onion. And now. . . . (*Sniff, sniff. Sounds of* GIANT *crying*)

LUCKY: Look. The Giant's crying. He can't see straight.

LULA (*Fast running footsteps*): Run!

LUCKY: Here's the front door. Hurry! He's coming after us.

CARROT: Your turn, Banana. Watch his step. (BANANA *trips* GIANT.)

GIANT: Whoa! (*Sound of bump*)

BEET: He slipped.

LULA: This way. Here's the gate.

19

LUCKY: We made it! We . . . . Oh, no! There's a guard at the gate.

GUARD: Off with your head.

LULA: Whose head?

GUARD: I don't care whose head. My orders are to stand here and say, "Off with your head," and get a head.

LETTUCE: That's me. So long, folks.

RADISH: Thanks, Lettuce.

LUCKY: Come on, Lula. Run!

LULA: Thanks for everything, Lettuce.

SCENE 6

SETTING: *In Mr. Farmer's vegetable garden*

LUCKY: Well, we didn't get that pot of gold.

LULA: But you did rescue me from the mean old giant.

LUCKY: It would be nice to surprise my mother with the pot of gold, though. . . . (*Thinks for a minute*) I know! I'll get her a four *karat* ring.

LULA (*Surprised*): How are you going to do that? You don't have any money for that . . . .(*Smiles, realizing the joke*) Oh, you mean a four *carrot* ring.

LUCKY (*Looking around the vegetable garden*): You know, I never thought the day would come when I would actually like vegetables.

The End

African Trio

Three folk tales from Africa

by Barbara Winther

I. *The Fierce Creature*

Characters

THREE STORYTELLERS
CATERPILLAR
HARE
LEOPARD
RHINOCEROS
ELEPHANT
FROG

Reprinted from *Dramatized Folk Tales of the World,* edited by
Sylvia E. Kamerman, Plays, Inc., Publishers, Boston, Mass. 02116.
Copyright © 1969 by Plays, Inc.

BEFORE RISE: THREE STORYTELLERS *enter before curtain and sit on three stools at left.* 2ND STORYTELLER *beats African drum during opening lines.*

1ST STORYTELLER: Listen!

3RD STORYTELLER: Listen!

2ND STORYTELLER: Listen to a continent!

1ST STORYTELLER: Listen!

1ST *and* 2ND STORYTELLERS: Listen!

ALL: Listen to the rhythm. Boom, boom, boom, boom. Boomity boom, boom, boom.

2ND STORYTELLER: African beat! (1ST *and* 3RD STORYTELLERS *slap thighs.*) Up through your feet! (*All stamp feet.*)

1ST *and* 3RD STORYTELLERS: Telling the folk tales . . .

2ND STORYTELLER: Native, tribal folk tales . . .

ALL: *Of* — (*They pause, then shout.*) Africa! (2ND STORYTELLER *stops beating drum.*)

1ST STORYTELLER (*Rising*): The story I shall tell you is from Eastern Africa. It is told by the tall Masai who live in the high country of Kenya. It is the story of "The Fierce Creature." (*Curtain opens.*)

SETTING: *The stage is bare. A slide of East Africa is projected on the screen which serves as a backdrop.*
AT RISE: *Stagehand carries in a large cutout of a Masai house.*

1ST STORYTELLER: A caterpillar came crawling along, looking for a place to rest. He entered the house of the hare. (*As he speaks,* CATERPILLAR *crawls onstage and enters house.*) When the hare came home he noticed

22

strange marks on the ground in front of his house. (HARE *enters and inspects ground in front of house.*)

HARE (*Shouting*): Who is in my house?

1ST STORYTELLER: The caterpillar did not want to be eaten by the hare, so he answered in a fierce voice.

CATERPILLAR (*From inside house*): I am the terrible warrior, deadlier than the leopard. I crush the rhinoceros to earth and trample the mighty elephant.

1ST STORYTELLER: The hare was most frightened. (HARE *hops about and trembles.*) He didn't know what to do, so when the leopard came padding by, searching for meat, the hare stopped her. (LEOPARD *roars off left, then enters stealthily, sniffing wind.*)

HARE: There is a fierce creature in my house, leopard. (LEOPARD *crosses to house, sniffing stage.*)

LEOPARD (*Loudly*): Who is in the hare's house?

CATERPILLAR (*Fiercely*): I am the terrible warrior, deadlier than the leopard. I crush the rhinoceros to earth and trample the mighty elephant. (LEOPARD *yelps in fear and hides behind* HARE.)

1ST STORYTELLER: Soon a rhinoceros came charging by on his way to the water hole. (RHINOCEROS *snorts off left, and enters, charging, with his horn lowered.*)

HARE: Can you help me, rhinoceros? There is a fierce creature in my house. (RHINOCEROS *snorts, then charges to* HARE's *house.*)

RHINOCEROS (*Loudly*): Who is in the hare's house?

CATERPILLAR (*Fiercely*): I am the terrible warrior, deadlier than the leopard. I crush the rhinoceros to earth and trample the mighty elephant. (RHINOCEROS *snorts and hides behind* LEOPARD.)

23

1ST STORYTELLER: Soon an elephant came lumbering by, looking for bananas. (ELEPHANT *trumpets off left, then lumbers in, pretending to look in trees.*)

HARE: Can you help us, elephant? There is a fierce creature in my house. (ELEPHANT *lumbers to house.*)

ELEPHANT (*Loudly*): Who is in the hare's house?

CATERPILLAR (*Fiercely*): I am the terrible warrior, deadlier than the leopard. I crush the rhinoceros to earth, and trample the mighty elephant. (ELEPHANT *trumpets and hides behind* RHINOCEROS.)

1ST STORYTELLER: Finally, a clever frog came hopping by on his way to catch bugs. (FROG *croaks and enters, hopping.*)

HARE: Frog, can you help me? There is a fierce creature in my house. (FROG *hops to house.*)

FROG: Who is in the hare's house?

CATERPILLAR: I am the terrible warrior, deadlier than the leopard. I crush the rhinoceros to earth and trample the mighty elephant.

FROG (*Shouting*): I, the hideous leaper, have come. I am slimy, green, full of great, big warts. (CATERPILLAR *squeaks in fear and crawls out of* HARE's *house and off right.*)

CATERPILLAR (*Exciting*): Help! Help! (*Animals watch him go, then fall down laughing.*)

FROG (*Bowing*): Kindly excuse me. I believe I just saw a fierce creature come crawling out of the hare's house. I, the terrible warrior, will pursue him, for my dinner is long past due. (*Exits right, hopping;* 1ST STORY-TELLER *sits. Curtain.*)

II. *When the Hare Brought the Sun*

Characters

THREE STORYTELLERS
HEADMAN
CHIEF
SUN GIRL
MOON GIRL
HARE
PURSUERS

BEFORE RISE: THREE STORYTELLERS *remain seated.* 2ND STORYTELLER *begins to beat drum.*

1ST STORYTELLER: Listen!

3RD STORYTELLER: Listen!

2ND STORYTELLER: Listen to a continent.

1ST STORYTELLER: Listen!

1ST *and* 3RD STORYTELLER: Listen!

ALL: Listen to the rhythm. Boom, boom, boom, boom, Boomity boom, boom, boom.

2ND STORYTELLER: African beat! African beat! (1ST *and* 3RD STORYTELLERS *slap thighs.*) Up through your feet! (*All stamp feet.*)

1ST *and* 3RD STORYTELLERS: Telling the folk tales . . .

2ND STORYTELLER: Native, tribal folk tales . . .

ALL: Of — (*Pause, then shout*) Africa! (*Drum stops.*)

2ND STORYTELLER (*Rising*): I shall tell another story of the hare. It is told among the tribes who live on the flat grasslands of the veld in Southern Africa. It is called, "When the Hare Brought the Sun." (*Curtain opens.*)

SETTING: *Bare stage. A view of South Africa is projected on the screen.*
AT RISE: 2ND STORYTELLER *begins narration.*

2ND STORYTELLER: In the early days when the earth had no sun or moon, the hare took his musical instrument, called the mbira, and climbed up a giant spider web to visit the great country which was up there. (HARE *enters, playing mbira, or another simple stringed instrument.*) He came to the village, seeking shelter. (*Stagehand carries on cutout of veld house.*)

HARE (*Looking at house, then calling loudly*): Where is the chief?

HEADMAN (*Entering right*): I am the headman of this village. Why do you wish to see the chief?

HARE: I will play my instrument for him if he gives me shelter.

27

HEADMAN (*Calling off right*): Great chief, there is a hare who comes to our village playing the mbira. He seeks shelter.

CHIEF (*Entering right; to* HARE): Play for me. (HARE *plays instrument and dances.*) You play well. I shall give you lodging in this house. (*Points to house*)

HARE: Thank you. I have had a tiring journey. It will be good to rest. (CHIEF *and* HEADMAN *exit.* HARE *enters house.*)

2ND STORYTELLER: That evening the hare looked out of his door and saw a girl sitting in front of two large pots. (MOON GIRL *enters right with a large red pot and a large yellow pot. She sits, and places pots before her.* HARE *peers out of door and watches. Suddenly,* SUN GIRL *enters, running, carrying a large red disc.*)

SUN GIRL: I bring the sun back from our sky. (*Puts disc in red pot.*)

MOON GIRL: Then it is time for me to hang out the moon. (*Takes yellow disc from yellow pot and exits*)

SUN GIRL: It is time for me to go to bed. (*Yawns and exits*)

HARE (*Creeping out of house*): It would be a fine thing for my world below to have some of that sun. (*He takes red disc from red pot and tears off a piece of it.*) I'll climb back down the spider web to earth. (*Runs off right*)

2ND STORYTELLER: The next morning the two girls returned.

MOON GIRL (*Entering left with yellow disc*): It is time for me to rest. (*Puts yellow disc in yellow pot*)

SUN GIRL (*Entering*): It is time for me to hang out the sun. (*Reaches into red pot*) Something is wrong with the sun! (*Pulls out torn disc*) Look! Part of it is missing. Someone has stolen part of the sun! (HEADMAN *and* CHIEF *rush on from right.*)

CHIEF: How dare anybody do such a thing?

HEADMAN (*Looking at ground and pointing*): It must have been the hare. These are his footprints.

CHIEF: We shall follow him. (CHIEF *and* HEADMAN *exit left, running.* SUN GIRL *and* MOON GIRL *follow, carrying pots. House is removed.*)

2ND STORYTELLER: The chief and his headman climbed down the great spider web to earth, and called together the animals to pursue the hare. (HARE *enters left and runs across stage in "slow motion."* CHIEF, HEADMAN, *and* PURSUERS — *animals from first play* — *enter left in single file and move after* HARE, *also in "slow motion."*) As the pursuers drew closer, the hare threw the three-spiked devil thorns across his trail. (HARE *pantomimes throwing thorns.* CHIEF, HEADMAN, *and* PURSUERS *cry out in pain as they step on "thorns," rub feet or paws, and continue to track* HARE.) The hare pulled down huge vines to block his path. (HARE *pantomimes pulling down vines, and others pantomime fighting through them.*) The hare caused a great rain to wash away his footprints. (HARE *points to sky and others cover heads with hands, peering closer to ground.*) The hare came to a stream. He lay down and turned into a log. (HARE *lies down and remains motionless.*)

CHIEF (*Stopping and looking around*): I don't see the hare's footprints anymore.

HEADMAN: Neither do I.

1ST PURSUER (*Sniffing*): We don't smell him, either.

CHIEF: I guess we've lost him. Come on, let's go home. (*In single file, CHIEF, HEADMAN, and PURSUERS pretend to walk across "log" and exit. HARE jumps up and leaps for joy.*)

2ND STORYTELLER: So the hare gave the sun to the earth, and we have had it ever since that day. (*HARE waves "sun" as curtains close.*)

31

III. *The Princess Who Was Hidden from the World*

Characters

THREE STORYTELLERS
OLD CHIEF
PRINCESS
YOUNG CHIEF
SERVANT GIRL
EMISSARY
PROPERTY GIRL

BEFORE RISE: 2ND STORYTELLER *beats drum.*

1ST STORYTELLER: Listen!

3RD STORYTELLER: Listen!

2ND STORYTELLER: Listen to a continent.

1ST STORYTELLER: Listen!

1ST *and* 3RD STORYTELLERS: Listen!

ALL: Listen to the rhythm. Boom, boom, boom, boom. Boomity boom, boom, boom.

2ND STORYTELLER: African beat! African beat! (1ST *and* 3RD STORYTELLERS *slap thighs.*) Up through your feet! (*All stamp feet.*)

1ST *and* 3RD STORYTELLERS: Telling the folk tales . . .

2ND STORYTELLER: Native, tribal folk tales . . .

ALL: Of — (*Pause, then shout*) Africa! (*Drum stops.*)

3RD STORYTELLER (*Standing*): The story I shall tell you is from Western Africa. It is told by the Vai tribe in the rain forests of Liberia. The name of the story is "The Princess Who Was Hidden from the World." (*Curtains open.*)

SETTING: *Slide of Liberia is projected on screen. Liberian house is at right.*
AT RISE: OLD CHIEF *enters.*

3RD STORYTELLER: There was an old chief who was very good but not very wise. He had a beautiful daughter. (PRINCESS *enters and stands by* OLD CHIEF.) Although she was well trained in being a princess (PRINCESS *poses gracefully.*), she was kept hidden away from the world. (OLD CHIEF *puts his hand over his daughter's eyes and peers about suspiciously.*) The young chief of another tribe heard about this lovely girl. (YOUNG CHIEF *and* EMISSARY *enter at left.*) He sent an emissary with gifts and an offer of marriage. (YOUNG CHIEF *pantomimes handing gifts to* EMISSARY, *who staggers under their weight, then crosses to* OLD CHIEF.) The old chief agreed to the marriage. (OLD CHIEF *nods happily as he examines gifts.* EMISSARY *exits left.*) He called for a servant girl to take his daughter to marry the young tribal chief. (OLD CHIEF *beckons off right.* SERVANT GIRL *enters and takes* PRINCESS's *hand.* OLD CHIEF *smiles happily and exits.*) The servant girl and the princess traveled through the rain forest. (PRINCESS *follows* SERVANT GIRL *offstage.* PROPERTY GIRL *enters, carrying long blue streamers, and stands at center.*)

PRINCESS (*Entering and seeing waterfall*): Look! The water is flowing down over the rocks. What is this?

SERVANT (*Following her*): It is a waterfall.

PRINCESS: Tell me about it.

SERVANT (*Sadly*): I can only tell you the story for a price. If I told you the story for nothing you would become terribly ill.

PRINCESS: What is the price?

SERVANT: Your sandals.

PRINCESS (*Taking off sandals*): Take them. (*They exchange sandals.*)

3RD STORYTELLER: Then the servant girl told the story of how the waterfall flowed down to join a big river, and how the river flowed out to join the big ocean. The princess was amazed, and she walked on through the rain forest, thinking of all she had heard. (PRINCESS *and* SERVANT GIRL *exit, followed by* PROPERTY GIRL, *who re-enters with cutout of a palm tree.*)

PRINCESS (*Re-entering; seeing tree*): What is this?

SERVANT (*Following*): It is a palm tree.

PRINCESS: Tell me about it.

SERVANT: I can only tell you the story for a price.

PRINCESS: What is the price?

SERVANT: Your headdress.

PRINCESS: Here. (*Gives headdress to* SERVANT *to wear*)

3RD STORYTELLER: Then the servant girl told the story of palm trees and many other trees, and how some bore delicious fruit and others gave their wood. The princess was amazed, and she walked on through the rain forest, thinking of all she had heard. (PRINCESS *and* SERVANT GIRL *exit, followed by* PROPERTY GIRL, *who re-enters with model of a peacock.*)

PRINCESS (*Re-entering*): What is this beautiful creature?

SERVANT (*Following her*): It is a peacock.

PRINCESS: Tell me about it.

SERVANT (*Sadly*): I can only tell you the story for a price.

PRINCESS: What is the price?

SERVANT: Your royal cloak and jewels.

PRINCESS: Take them. (*Hands cloak and jewels to* SERVANT GIRL, *who puts them on*)

3RD STORYTELLER: The servant girl told the princess all about peacocks and other animals, those that flew, those that swam, those that crawled, and those that ran. The princess was amazed, and she walked on through the rain forest, thinking of all she had heard. (PRINCESS *exits, followed by* SERVANT GIRL *and* PROPERTY GIRL, *who re-enters with cut-out of a rainbow.*)

PRINCESS (*Re-entering, followed by* SERVANT GIRL): What is that beautiful sight in the sky?

SERVANT GIRL: It is a rainbow.

PRINCESS: Tell me about it.

SERVANT: This is the greatest secret of all, so the price is the most.

PRINCESS: What is the price?

SERVANT: You must promise never to tell that you are a princess and I am a servant girl.

PRINCESS: I agree.

3RD STORYTELLER: Then the servant girl told the story of the sun shining through the water in the sky. She told about the clouds and the storms and the white, cold powder that fell on the high mountains far to the east. The princess was amazed, and she walked on to the village, thinking of all she had heard. (PRINCESS *and* SERVANT GIRL *exit, followed by* PROPERTY GIRL, *who re-enters with Liberian house and stands it at left.* YOUNG CHIEF *enters left and stands by house.*) When the princess and the servant girl came to the village, the young chief mistook the servant girl for the princess, and he married her. (PRINCESS *and* SERVANT GIRL *enter right and cross to* YOUNG CHIEF, *who beckons to*

SERVANT GIRL *to follow. They exit into house.*) Even
though the real princess was treated as a servant and
had to crush casava roots and rice all day long, she was
so kind and good that everybody loved her. (PRINCESS
pantomimes pounding roots.) But the servant girl
acted as she thought a princess should. She was selfish
and cruel, and everybody disliked her. (SERVANT GIRL
struts out of house, pretends to kick PRINCESS, *and
struts around with her nose in the air.* PRINCESS *exits.*)
Several years later, the father of the real princess came
to the village to visit his daughter. (OLD CHIEF *enters.*
SERVANT GIRL *sees him and runs to hide in house.*
YOUNG CHIEF *enters and shakes hands with* OLD
CHIEF.)

OLD CHIEF: Where is my daughter?

YOUNG CHIEF (*Pointing to house*): In there, and I would be most happy if you would take her away.

OLD CHIEF (*Peering into house*): That is not my daughter!

YOUNG CHIEF: That is not your daughter? (PRINCESS *enters. Seeing* OLD CHIEF, *she kneels at his feet.*)

OLD CHIEF: This is my daughter!

YOUNG CHIEF: That is your daughter? I've been deceived. (*He pulls* SERVANT GIRL *out of house and shoos her off left. To* PRINCESS) You shall be my wife. (*He enters house and* PRINCESS *follows him.*)

OLD CHIEF: Now I realize that I should have taught my daughter more about the world! I'm a wiser man than I was when I left my village. (*Taps head and exits. Curtains close.* STORYTELLERS *exit, dancing and beating drums.*)

The End

The Wizard of Oz

by L. Frank Baum

Adapted by Lynne Sharon Schwartz

Characters

NARRATOR
DOROTHY
WITCH OF THE NORTH
THREE MUNCHKINS
SCARECROW
TIN WOODMAN
COWARDLY LION
SOLDIER
WIZARD OF OZ
LOVELY LADY
WICKED WITCH OF THE WEST
KING OF THE WINGED MONKEYS
WINGED MONKEYS
GLINDA, *the Good Witch of the South*
AUNT EM

SCENE 1

BEFORE RISE: NARRATOR *enters and goes to a lectern at one side in front of curtain.*

Reprinted from *Fifty Plays for Junior Actors*, edited by Sylvia E. Kamerman, Plays, Inc., Publishers, Boston, Mass. 02116. Copyright © 1963 by Plays, Inc.

NARRATOR: Once upon a time there was a little girl named Dorothy, who lived in the great Kansas prairies with her Uncle Henry, who was a farmer, and her Aunt Em, and her dog, Toto.

One day they heard a low wail of the wind, and they saw the long grass bowing in waves; they heard a sharp, whistling sound in the air, and they knew that a great storm, a cyclone, was coming. (*Howling sound of wind is heard from offstage.*) Uncle Henry ran out to take care of the cattle, and Aunt Em ran to a trapdoor in the floor, calling to Dorothy to follow her. But at that moment Toto jumped out of Dorothy's arms and hid under the bed. As Dorothy reached to get him, the house shook so hard that she lost her footing and fell down on the floor. Then the house whirled around two or three times and rose slowly through the air, and Dorothy felt as if she were going up in a balloon. The house was in the exact center of the cyclone, and it was carried miles and miles up into the air. The wind was shrieking loudly, but soon the house felt very calm, and Dorothy crawled into her bed and fell asleep. When she awoke, she found herself in a strange place. (NARRATOR *exits as curtain rises.*)

SETTING: *A field. A backdrop portrays the front of a cottage. Two silver shoes can be seen sticking out from under the house.*

AT RISE: DOROTHY *is standing near the doorway holding her dog, Toto.*

DOROTHY: I wonder where I am! All I can remember is whirling around and around. (*Looks around.*

WITCH OF THE NORTH *and* THREE MUNCHKINS *enter.*)

WITCH OF THE NORTH (*Going to* DOROTHY *and bowing*): You are welcome, most noble Sorceress, to the land of the Munchkins. We are so grateful to you for having killed the Wicked Witch of the East, and for setting our people free from bondage.

DOROTHY: You are very kind, but there must be some mistake. I have not killed anyone.

WITCH OF THE NORTH (*Laughing*): Your house did, anyway, and that is the same thing. See! (*She points to the corner of the house.*) There are her two feet, sticking out from under the house.

DOROTHY (*Dismayed*): Oh, dear. The house must have fallen on her. Whatever shall we do?

WITCH OF THE NORTH: There is nothing to be done. She was the Wicked Witch of the East, and she made the Munchkins her slaves. Now they are set free, and are grateful to you.

DOROTHY: Who are the Munchkins?

WITCH OF THE NORTH: They are the people who live in this land of the East. These are three of my Munchkin friends. (THREE MUNCHKINS *bow to* DOROTHY.) I am the Witch of the North.

DOROTHY: Oh, gracious! Are you a real witch?

WITCH OF THE NORTH: Yes, indeed. But I am a good witch, and the people love me.

DOROTHY: I thought all witches were wicked.

WITCH OF THE NORTH: Oh, no, that is a great mistake. There were four witches in all the Land of Oz, and two of them, those who live in the North and the

41

South, are good witches. Those who lived in the East and the West were wicked witches; but now that you have killed the Wicked Witch of the East, there is but one Wicked Witch left, the one who lives in the West.

1ST MUNCHKIN (*Who has been peering at the feet of the Wicked Witch*): Look! Look! Her feet have disappeared. (*All run to look.*)

WITCH OF THE NORTH: She was so old that she dried up quickly in the sun. That is the end of her. But the silver shoes are yours, and you shall have them to wear. (*Gives shoes to* DOROTHY)

2ND MUNCHKIN: There is some charm connected with these silver shoes, but what it is, we never knew.

DOROTHY: Thank you. (*Puts shoes on*) Now, can you
  help me find my way back to my aunt and uncle?
3RD MUNCHKIN: There is a great desert all around this
  land, and no one can live to cross it.
WITCH OF THE NORTH: I am afraid, my dear, that you
  will have to live with us.
DOROTHY (*Starting to cry*): But I want to go back to
  Kansas.
WITCH OF THE NORTH (*Taking off her cap and looking
  inside*): Perhaps we will get a magic message from
  the cap to help us. (*Reading*) It says, "Let Dorothy
  go to the City of Emeralds." Is your name Dorothy, my dear?
DOROTHY: Yes. Where is the City of Emeralds?
WITCH OF THE NORTH: It is in the center of the country,
  and is ruled by Oz, the Great Wizard.

DOROTHY: Is he a good man?

WITCH OF THE NORTH: He is a good Wizard. Whether he is a man or not I cannot tell, for I have never seen him.

DOROTHY: How can I get there?

WITCH OF THE NORTH: You must walk. It is a long journey, through a country that is sometimes pleasant and sometimes dark and terrible. However, I will use all the magic arts I know of to keep you from harm, and I will give you my kiss. No one will dare injure a person who has been kissed by the Witch of the North. (*Kisses* DOROTHY *on the forehead*) The road to the City of Emeralds is paved with yellow brick, so you cannot miss it. When you get to Oz, do not be afraid of him, but tell him your story and ask him to help you. Goodbye, my dear.

MUNCHKINS (*Bowing*): Goodbye, Dorothy.

DOROTHY: Goodbye, and thank you. I will start on my journey right away. (WITCH *and* MUNCHKINS *exit. Lights dim to indicate the passage of time. While the stage is dark, the* SCARECROW *enters and stands on a high stool at one side. There is a pole in back of the stool which he pretends to be attached to. When the lights come up,* DOROTHY *is walking across the stage, holding Toto. Suddenly she notices the* SCARECROW.) I'm sure I saw the Scarecrow wink at me, but it couldn't be. He's just made of straw.

SCARECROW: Good day.

DOROTHY (*Surprised*): Did you speak?

SCARECROW: Certainly. How do you do?

DOROTHY: I'm pretty well, thank you. How do you do?

SCARECROW: I'm not feeling well. It's very tedious being perched up here night and day to scare away crows.

DOROTHY: Can't you get down?

SCARECROW: No, because this pole is stuck up my back. If you will please take away the pole, I shall be greatly obliged to you. (DOROTHY *goes to* SCARECROW *and pretends to lift him off pole. He steps down and lowers his arms.*) Thank you very much. I feel like a new man. (*Stretches and yawns*) Who are you, and where are you going?

DOROTHY: My name is Dorothy, and I am going to the Emerald City to ask the great Oz to send me back to Kansas.

SCARECROW: Where is the Emerald City? And who is Oz?

DOROTHY: Why, don't you know?

SCARECROW (*Sadly*): No, indeed; I don't know anything. You see, I am stuffed, so I have no brains at all.

DOROTHY: Oh, I'm awfully sorry.

SCARECROW: Do you think if I go to the Emerald City with you, that Oz would give me some brains?

DOROTHY: I cannot tell, but you may come with me if you like.

SCARECROW: I think I shall. You see, I don't mind my legs and arms and body being stuffed, because I cannot get hurt. But I don't like to be thought a fool. (*As they talk,* TIN WOODMAN *enters, unseen by the others, and stands at one side of the stage with his ax raised; he groans, first softly, then louder.*)

DOROTHY (*Looking around*): I'm sure I heard someone groan. (*Sees* TIN WOODMAN *and goes to him*) Oh! Did you groan?

TIN WOODMAN: Yes, I did. I've been groaning for more than a year.

DOROTHY (*Sympathetically*): What can I do for you?

TIN WOODMAN: Get an oilcan and oil my joints. They are rusted so badly that I cannot move them at all. You will find an oilcan right in front of my cottage a few steps further in the woods.

DOROTHY: Very well. You wait here. (*Pause*) Of course, you must wait here, for you can't move. (*She runs offstage and returns immediately carrying oilcan.*) Where are your joints?

TIN WOODMAN: Oil my neck, first. (DOROTHY *does so.* SCARECROW *helps by moving* TIN WOODMAN's *head from side to side gently.*) Now oil the joints in my arms. (DOROTHY *does so.* SCARECROW *bends* TIN WOODMAN's *arms.* TIN WOODMAN *sighs and lowers his ax.*) This is a great comfort. I have been holding that ax in the air ever since I rusted in a rainstorm, and I'm glad to be able to put it down at last. Now, if you will oil the joints of my legs, I shall be all right once more. (*They oil his legs.*) Thank you so much. I might have stood there always if you had not come along, so you have certainly saved my life. How did you happen to be here?

DOROTHY: We are on our way to the Emerald City to see the Great Oz. I want him to send me back to Kansas, and the Scarecrow wants him to put a few brains into his head.

TIN WOODMAN (*After thinking for a moment*): Do you suppose Oz could give me a heart?

DOROTHY: Why, I guess so. It would be as easy as giving the Scarecrow brains.

TIN WOODMAN: True. If you will allow me to join your party, I will also go to the Emerald City and ask Oz to help me.

SCARECROW: Come along. We'd be pleased to have you. But if I were you, I should ask for brains instead of a heart, for a fool with no brains would not know what to do with a heart if he had one.

TIN WOODMAN: I shall take the heart, for brains do not make one happy, and happiness is the best thing in the world. (*A great roar is heard, and the* COWARDLY LION *rushes in. He knocks the* SCARECROW *over, and strikes the* TIN WOODMAN, *who falls to the ground.* DOROTHY *drops Toto, in her surprise, and the* LION *rushes toward him.* DOROTHY *snatches him up, and then slaps the* LION *on the nose.*)

DOROTHY: Don't you dare to bite Toto! You ought to be ashamed of yourself, a big beast like you, biting a poor little dog!

LION (*Rubbing his nose*): I didn't bite him.

DOROTHY: No, but you tried to. You are nothing but a big coward.

LION (*Hanging his head in shame*): I know it. I've always known it. But how can I help it?

DOROTHY: I'm sure I don't know. To think of your striking a stuffed man like the poor Scarecrow!

LION: Is he stuffed?

DOROTHY (*Helping the* SCARECROW *up and patting his clothes into shape*): Of course he's stuffed.

LION: That's why he went over so easily. Is the other one stuffed also?

DOROTHY (*Helping* TIN WOODMAN *up*): No, he's made of tin.

LION: Then that's why he nearly blunted my claws.

SCARECROW: What makes you a coward?

LION: It's a mystery. I suppose I was born that way. All the other animals in the forest naturally expect me to be brave, for the Lion is everywhere thought to be the King of Beasts. I learned that if I roared very loudly every living thing was frightened and got out of my way. If the elephants and the tigers and the bears had ever tried to fight me, I should have run myself — I'm such a coward. But just as soon as they hear me roar they all try to get away from me, and of course I let them go.

SCARECROW: But that isn't right. The King of Beasts shouldn't be a coward.

LION: I know it. (*He wipes a tear from his eye with the tip of his tail.*) It is my great sorrow, and it makes my life very unhappy. But whenever there is danger, my heart begins to beat fast.

TIN WOODMAN: You ought to be glad of that, for it proves you have a heart. I have no heart at all, so it cannot beat fast. But I am going to the Great Oz to ask him for one.

SCARECROW: And I am going to ask him to give me brains, for my head is stuffed with straw.

DOROTHY: And I am going to ask him to send Toto and me back to Kansas.

LION: Do you think Oz could give me courage?

SCARECROW: Just as easily as he could give me brains.

TIN WOODMAN: Or give me a heart.

DOROTHY: Or send me back to Kansas.

LION: Then, if you don't mind, I'll go with you, for my life is simply unbearable without a bit of courage.

DOROTHY: You will be very welcome, for you will help to keep away the other wild beasts. I think it will be a long and difficult journey. (*They start to exit as curtain falls.*)

SCENE 2

TIME: *A few days later.*

SETTING: *Outside of Oz's throne room.*

BEFORE RISE: DOROTHY, SCARECROW, TIN WOODMAN, *and* LION *enter, all wearing green spectacles.*

DOROTHY: I am so glad to be here. I thought we would never arrive.

TIN WOODMAN: Let us hope that the Great Oz will see us. The soldier said that no one has asked to see Oz in many, many years. (SOLDIER *enters.*)

DOROTHY (*To* SOLDIER): Have you seen Oz and asked him about us?

SOLDIER: Oh, no, I have never seen him, but I gave him your message. When I mentioned your silver shoes he was very much interested. He said he would grant you an audience, but if you come on an idle or foolish errand he may be angry and destroy you all in an instant.

SCARECROW: But it is not a foolish errand, nor an idle one. It is important.

SOLDIER: Very well, then. But each of you must enter

his presence alone. And you must not remove the green spectacles.

DOROTHY: Why?

SOLDIER: Because that is the rule. Otherwise the brightness and glory of the Emerald City would blind you.

DOROTHY: Thank you. That is very kind of Oz. (*Bell rings.*)

SOLDIER: That is the signal. You must go into the throne room by yourself. (SOLDIER *exits with* SCARECROW, TIN WOODMAN, *and* LION, *as curtain rises.*)

SETTING: *The throne room. All the furnishings are green. Suspended over the throne at center is a tremendous papier-mâché head, with a mouth that moves.*

AT RISE: DOROTHY *walks hesitantly into room.*

OZ (*Speaking while hidden behind screen at one side*): I am Oz, the Great and Terrible. Who are you, and why do you seek me?

DOROTHY (*Speaking to the head*): I am Dorothy, the Small and Meek. I have come to you for help.

OZ: Where did you get the silver shoes?

DOROTHY: I got them from the Wicked Witch of the East, when my house fell on her and killed her.

OZ: What do you wish me to do?

DOROTHY: Send me back to Kansas, where my Aunt Em and Uncle Henry are. I am sure Aunt Em will be dreadfully worried over my being away so long.

OZ: Why should I do this for you?

DOROTHY: Because you are strong and I am weak; because you are a Great Wizard and I am only a helpless little girl.

Oz: But you were strong enough to kill the Wicked Witch of the East.

DOROTHY: That just happened. I could not help it.

Oz: Well, I will give you my answer. You have no right to expect me to send you back to Kansas unless you do something for me in return. Kill the Wicked Witch of the West.

DOROTHY: But I cannot!

Oz: You killed the Wicked Witch of the East, and you wear the silver shoes, which have a powerful charm. There is now but one Wicked Witch left in all this land, and when you can tell me she is dead, I will send you back to Kansas — but not before.

DOROTHY (*Beginning to weep*): I never killed anything, willingly, and even if I wanted to, how could I kill the Wicked Witch? If you, who are Great and Terrible, cannot kill her yourself, how do you expect me to do it?

Oz: I do not know, but that is my answer, and until the Wicked Witch of the West dies, you will not see your uncle and aunt again. Remember that the Witch is wicked — tremendously wicked — and ought to be killed. Now go, and do not ask to see me again until you have done your task. (*Blackout, during which* DOROTHY *exits; head is removed, and the* LOVELY LADY *enters and sits on the throne. Lights come up.* SCARECROW *enters and bows.*)

LADY: I am Oz, the Great and Terrible. Who are you, and why do you seek me?

SCARECROW: I am only a Scarecrow, stuffed with straw, and I have no brains. I come to you praying that you will put brains in my head instead of straw, so that I may become as much a man as any other.

LADY: Why should I do this for you?

SCARECROW: Because you are wise and powerful, and no one else can help me.

LADY: I never grant favors without some return, but this much I will promise. If you will kill the Wicked Witch of the West for me, I will bestow upon you a great many brains, and such good brains that you will be the wisest man in all the Land of Oz.

SCARECROW (*Surprised*): I thought you asked Dorothy to kill the Witch.

LADY: So I did. I don't care who kills her. Until she is dead I will not grant your wish. Now go, and do not seek me again until you have earned the brains you so greatly desire. (*Blackout, during which* SCARECROW *and* LADY *exit;* Oz *appears and sits on the throne, as a horrible beast. Lights up.* TIN WOODMAN *enters.* Oz *roars.*)

OZ: I am Oz, the Great and Terrible. Who are you, and why do you seek me?

TIN WOODMAN: I am a Woodman, and made of tin. Therefore I have no heart, and cannot love. I pray you to give me a heart that I may be as other men are.

OZ: Why should I do this?

TIN WOODMAN: Because I ask it, and you alone can grant my request.

Oz: If you indeed desire a heart, you must earn it.

Tin Woodman: How?

Oz: Help Dorothy kill the Wicked Witch of the West. When the Witch is dead, come to me and I will then give you the biggest and kindest and most loving heart in all the Land of Oz. (*He roars again as the lights black out, and he goes behind the screen.* Tin Woodman *exits. When lights go on again, there is a great "Ball of Fire" hanging over the throne.* Cowardly Lion *enters, frightened.*)

Oz (*Behind screen*): I am Oz, the Great and Terrible. Who are you, and why do you seek me?

Lion: I am a Cowardly Lion, though I am supposed to be King of the Beasts. I am frightened of everything I see, and so I have come to you to ask if you will give me courage.

Oz: Why should I do this for you?

Lion: Because you are great and powerful, and you alone can help me.

Oz: I will grant you courage only if you will do something for me. Help Dorothy kill the Wicked Witch of the West.

Lion: But how can I do that if I am a coward?

Oz: I do not know, but after you have killed her, you may come back to me and I will make you the most courageous beast in all the forest. Remember, I am Oz, the Great and Terrible. (*The Ball of Fire shakes in the air, and the* Lion *cringes as the curtain falls.*)

SCENE 3

BEFORE RISE: NARRATOR *enters and goes to lectern.*

NARRATOR: The next morning the four friends met and marveled at the many forms the Great Wizard could take. Then they started for the castle of the Wicked Witch of the West. At night, Dorothy and Toto and the Lion lay down to sleep, while the Scarecrow and the Tin Woodman kept watch.

Now, the Wicked Witch of the West had an eye that was as powerful as a telescope and could see everywhere. As she stood in front of her castle she looked out and saw Dorothy lying asleep with her friends around her. She was furious to find them in her country, and tried many ways to capture them, but was unsuccessful. She was a powerful witch, though, and thought of one last idea. (*Curtain slowly opens.*)

SETTING: *Before the castle of the Wicked Witch of the West. A backdrop depicts the front of the castle.*

AT RISE: WICKED WITCH *is onstage, holding a broom and a bucket of water; she peers around, then takes cap from her head.*

WICKED WITCH: The only way left to destroy these strangers is with the Golden Cap. This must be my last command to the Winged Monkeys, for I have commanded them twice already. (*Puts cap on her head and recites, first standing on left foot*) Ep-pe, pep-pe, kak-ke! (*Standing on right foot*) Hil-lo, hol-lo, hel-lo! (*Standing on both feet and crying out loudly*) Ziz-zy, zuz-zy, zik! (*A low, rumbling sound is heard and* WINGED MONKEYS *enter.*)

KING OF MONKEYS: You have called us for the third and last time. What do you command?

WICKED WITCH: Go to the strangers within my land and destroy them all except the Lion. Bring that beast to me, for I shall harness him like a horse, and make him work.

KING OF MONKEYS: Your commands shall be obeyed. (MONKEYS *run out.*)

NARRATOR: The Monkeys flew to Dorothy and her friends. First they seized the Tin Woodman and dropped him in a valley covered with sharp rocks, where he lay battered and dented. Then they caught the Scarecrow and pulled the straw out of his clothes. They made a small bundle of his hat and clothes and threw it into the branches of a tall tree. (NARRATOR *exits as* WINGED MONKEYS *enter with* DOROTHY, *who holds Toto.*)

KING OF MONKEYS (*To* WICKED WITCH): We have obeyed you as far as we are able. The Tin Woodman and the Scarecrow are destroyed, and the Lion is tied up in your yard. The little girl we dare not harm, nor the dog she carries with her, for the Witch of the North has kissed her forehead and left her mark. Your power over our band is now ended. (MONKEYS *exit.*)

WICKED WITCH (*To* DOROTHY): Aha! I have tried many ways to capture you, and at last I have you for my slave. See that you mind everything I tell you, for if you do not I will make an end of you. You will clean the pots and kettles and sweep the floor and tend the fire.

DOROTHY: You are a very wicked witch for destroying my friends and tying up the Lion, but your power

cannot last long. I have a special charm in my silver shoes that I got from the Wicked Witch of the East, and it will help me to get rid of you.

WICKED WITCH (*Staring at shoes*): The silver shoes! Give them to me!

DOROTHY: No!

WICKED WITCH (*Pushing* DOROTHY *down and grabbing one shoe*): There, you silly little girl. You cannot struggle against a powerful witch like me. Now I have your shoe and your charm will be useless.

DOROTHY: You wicked creature! You have no right to take my shoe from me.

WICKED WITCH: I shall keep it, just the same, and someday I shall get the other one from you, too.

DOROTHY (*In a rage*): Oh! (*Seizes bucket of water and dashes it over* WICKED WITCH, *who begins to shrink.* NOTE: *She does this by curling up slowly under her wide cloak and sinking to the floor, so that soon she is completely hidden under the cloak.*)

WICKED WITCH: See what you have done? In a minute I shall melt away.

DOROTHY (*Frightened and astonished*): I'm very sorry, indeed.

WICKED WITCH: Didn't you know water would be the end of me?

DOROTHY: Of course not. How could I?

WICKED WITCH: Well, in a minute I shall be all melted, and you will have the castle to yourself. I have been wicked in my day, but I never thought a little girl like you would ever be able to melt me and end my wicked deeds. Look out — here I go! (*Hides under cloak*)

DOROTHY (*Taking broom*): I may as well get her out of here. And take my shoe, too. (*Puts shoe back on*) Perhaps I shall take her Golden Cap also. (*Puts cap on*) It fits perfectly! (*She "sweeps" the* WICKED WITCH *offstage.*) Now I must go back to the Emerald City for my reward. But how can I save the Scarecrow and the Tin Woodman and the Lion? (*She looks about.*) And I am afraid I am hopelessly lost. What can I do? (*She sits down wearily, takes off the cap, and idly looks inside it.*) Oh, look! There's a charm in the cap! It's a magic rhyme. Maybe it will help me. (*Puts cap on and recites, standing on left foot*) Ep-pe, pep-pe, kak-ke! (*Stands on right foot*) Hil-lo, hol-lo, hel-lo! (*Louder, standing on both feet*) Ziz-zy, zuz-zy, zik! (WINGED MONKEYS *enter.*)

KING OF MONKEYS: What is your command? We can take you anywhere within the Land of Oz in a moment's time.

DOROTHY: I wish to go to the Emerald City, but I must rescue my friends and take them with me.

KING OF MONKEYS: We will carry you there, and we will find your friends and take them with us, have no fear. (MONKEYS *take* DOROTHY *and run offstage as curtain falls.*)

SCENE 4

SETTING: *Oz's throne room.*

AT RISE: *The throne is empty;* Oz *is hidden behind screen.* DOROTHY, SCARECROW, TIN WOODMAN, *and* LION *are onstage.*

DOROTHY: That was a good ride.

LION: Yes, and a quick way out of our troubles. How lucky it was that you took that wonderful cap, Dorothy.

DOROTHY: I wonder where Oz is. I don't see anything.

OZ (*From behind screen*): I am Oz, the Great and Terrible. Why do you seek me?

DOROTHY (*Looking around*): Where are you?

OZ: I am everywhere, but to the eyes of common mortals I am invisible.

DOROTHY: We have come to claim our rewards, O Great Oz.

OZ: What rewards?

DOROTHY: You promised to grant us all our wishes when the Wicked Witch was destroyed.

OZ: Is she really destroyed?

DOROTHY: Yes, I melted her with a bucket of water.

OZ: Dear me, how sudden. Well, come to me tomorrow, for I must have time to think it over.

TIN WOODMAN: You've had plenty of time already.

SCARECROW: We won't wait a day longer.

DOROTHY: You must keep your promises to us. (LION *lets out a great roar so that* DOROTHY *jumps, drops Toto, and tips over the screen. There is a crash, and they see a little old man with a bald head.*)

TIN WOODMAN (*Raising his ax and rushing toward* OZ): Who are you?

OZ: I am Oz, the Great and Terrible (*Trembles*), but don't strike me — please don't — and I'll do anything you want me to.

DOROTHY (*Dismayed*): I thought Oz was a great head.

SCARECROW: And I thought Oz was a lovely lady.

TIN WOODMAN: And I thought Oz was a terrible beast.

LION: And I thought he was a Ball of Fire.

OZ: No, you are all wrong. I have been making believe. I'm supposed to be a Great Wizard, but I'm just a common man.

SCARECROW: You're more than that. You're a humbug, a fake!

OZ: Exactly! (*Rubs his hands together in pleasure*) But don't speak so loudly or you will be overheard, and I shall be ruined.

TIN WOODMAN: But this is terrible. How shall I ever get my heart?

LION: Or I my courage?

SCARECROW: Or I my brains?

OZ: My dear friends, I pray you not to speak of these little things. Think of me, and the terrible trouble I'm in since you found me out.

DOROTHY: Doesn't anyone else know you're a humbug?

OZ: No one but the four of you.

DOROTHY (*Bewildered*): But I don't understand. How was it that you appeared to me as a great head?

OZ: That was one of my tricks. Everything has been a trick.

SCARECROW: Really, you ought to be ashamed of yourself for being such a humbug.

OZ: I am — I certainly am — but it was the only thing I could do. You see, I was born in Omaha —

DOROTHY: Why, that isn't very far from Kansas!

OZ: No, but it's farther from here. (*Shakes his head sadly*) I worked in a circus as a balloonist — that's a man who goes up in a balloon on circus day, to draw a crowd of people together. One day the ropes of my balloon got twisted, so that I couldn't come down again, and I floated miles through the air until I landed in this strange and beautiful country. The people here, who saw me come down gently from the clouds, thought I was a great wizard. They were afraid of me and promised to do anything I wished, so to amuse myself and to keep the good people busy I ordered them to build this city and my palace. Because the country was so green and beautiful I called it the Emerald City. I have been good to the people, and they like me. But one of my greatest fears was the Witches, who had magical powers, while I had none at all. That is why I was so pleased to hear that your house had fallen on the Wicked Witch of the East, and why I was so willing to promise anything if you would do away with the other Witch. But I am ashamed to say now that I cannot keep my promises.

DOROTHY: I think you are a very bad man.

OZ: Oh, no, my dear. I'm really a very good man, but I'm a very bad Wizard, I must admit.

SCARECROW: Can't you give me brains?

OZ: You don't need them. You are learning something every day. A baby has brains, but it doesn't know much. Experience is the only thing that brings knowledge, and the longer you are on earth the more experience you are sure to get.

SCARECROW: That may all be true, but I shall be very unhappy unless you give me brains.

Oz: Then I will try to give you brains. I cannot tell you how to use them, however; you must find that out for yourself. (Oz *goes to cabinet and fills a cup with powder, then goes to* SCARECROW *and pretends to pour the powder into his head.*) The main ingredient is bran. Hereafter you will be a great man, for I have given you a lot of brand-new brains!

SCARECROW: Oh, thank you, thank you. And I'll find a way to use them, never fear.

DOROTHY (*To* SCARECROW): How do you feel?

SCARECROW: I feel wise indeed.

LION: Now, how about my courage?

Oz: You have plenty of courage, I am sure. All you need is confidence in yourself. There is no living thing that is not afraid when it faces danger. True courage is facing danger when you are afraid, and you have plenty of true courage.

LION: Perhaps I have, but I'm scared just the same. I shall really be very unhappy unless you give me the sort of courage that makes one forget he is afraid.

Oz: Very well, I will get some for you. (*Goes to cupboard, takes down green bottle, and pours contents into a green dish. He offers it to the* LION, *who sniffs at it disdainfully.*) Drink.

LION: What is it?

Oz: Well, if it were inside of you, it would be courage. You know, of course, that courage is always inside a person; so that this really cannot be called courage until you have swallowed it. Therefore I advise you to drink it as soon as possible. (LION *drinks.*) How do you feel now?

LION (*Happily*): Full of courage!

TIN WOODMAN: How about my heart?

Oz: Why, as for that, I think you are wrong to want a heart. It makes most people unhappy. If you only knew it, you are in luck not to have a heart.

TIN WOODMAN: That must be a matter of opinion. For my part, I will bear all the unhappiness without a murmur, if you will give me a heart.

Oz: Very well. (*Goes to cabinet, takes out paper heart and pins it carefully on* TIN WOODMAN'*s chest*) Isn't it a beauty?

TIN WOODMAN (*Looking down at it*): It is, indeed. But is it a kind heart?

OZ: Oh, very kind. It is a heart that any man might be proud of.

TIN WOODMAN: I am very grateful to you, and shall never forget your kindness.

DOROTHY: And now, how am I to get back to Kansas?

OZ (*Sighs*): We shall have to think about that for a while. (*Curtain*)

SCENE 5

BEFORE RISE: NARRATOR *enters and goes to lectern.*

NARRATOR: Oz thought for several days, and finally decided that he and Dorothy should leave in a balloon. Dorothy worked hard on making the balloon and it was soon ready, but at the moment they were to take off, she realized that she had lost Toto. She hurried through the crowd looking for him, but by the time she found him the balloon was already sailing overhead, and Oz could not bring it back. She was very sad, and cried because she thought she would never get back to Kansas. Finally a soldier who felt sorry for Dorothy came and told her that Glinda, the Good Witch of the South, might help her. Glinda was the most powerful of all the Witches, and ruled over the Quadlings. The road to her castle was full of dangers to travelers, but Dorothy decided to go nevertheless, because it was her last hope, and her faithful friends went along to protect her. (NARRATOR *exits as curtain rises.*)

TIME: *A few days later.*

SETTING: *A room in Glinda's castle.*

AT RISE: DOROTHY, SCARECROW, TIN WOODMAN, *and* LION *enter.*

DOROTHY: This must be Glinda's castle. Isn't it beautiful?

TIN WOODMAN: She must be an especially good witch, and I know she will help you, Dorothy. (GLINDA *enters.*)

GLINDA: I am Glinda, the Good Witch of the South. I have heard of how you landed here on the cyclone, child. What can I do for you?

DOROTHY (*Curtsying*): My greatest wish is to get back to Kansas, for Aunt Em will certainly think something dreadful has happened to me.

GLINDA: I am sure I can help you. But if I do, you must give me the Golden Cap.

DOROTHY: Willingly, for it will be of no use to me now. (*Gives her cap*)

GLINDA: I think I will need it just three times. (*To* SCARECROW) What will you do when Dorothy has left us?

SCARECROW: I will return to the Emerald City, for Oz has made me its ruler, and the people like me. The only thing that worries me is how to cross the tremendous mountain bordering your land. On our journey here the Winged Monkeys carried us over.

GLINDA: By the Golden Cap I shall command the Winged Monkeys to carry you again to the gates of the Emerald City, for it would be a shame to deprive the people of so wonderful a ruler. (*To* TIN WOODMAN) What will become of you when Dorothy leaves?

TIN WOODMAN: The Winkies, in the land of the West, were very kind to me, and wanted me to rule over them after the Wicked Witch of the West was melted. If I could get back again, I should like nothing better than to be their ruler forever.

GLINDA: My second command to the Winged Monkeys will be that they carry you safely to the land of the Winkies. Your brains may not be as large as those of the Scarecrow, but you are really much brighter than he is when you are well polished — and I am sure you will rule the Winkies wisely and well. (*To* LION) When Dorothy has returned to her home, what will become of you?

LION: The beasts in the forest on the outskirts of your land have made me their king, because during our journey here I saved them from a wicked monster. If only I could get back to them I should pass my life there very happily.

GLINDA: My third command to the Winged Monkeys shall be to carry you to your forest. Then, having used up the powers of the Golden Cap, I shall give it to the King of the Monkeys, so that he and his band may be free forever after.

SCARECROW, TIN WOODMAN, LION (*Ad lib*): Thank you. You are so kind to us. (*Etc.*)

DOROTHY: You are certainly as good as you are beautiful. But you have not yet told me how to get back to Kansas.

GLINDA: Your silver shoes have wonderful powers. They can carry you across the desert, anywhere in the world. In fact, if you had known their power you could have gone back to your Aunt Em the very first day you came to this country.

SCARECROW: But then I should not have had my wonderful brains. I might have passed my whole life in the farmer's cornfield.

TIN WOODMAN: And I should not have had my lovely heart. I might have stood and rusted in the forest till the end of the world.

LION: And I should have lived a coward forever, and no beast in all the forest would have had a good word to say to me.

DOROTHY: This is all true, and I am glad I was of use to these good friends. But now that each of them has what he most desired, and a kingdom to rule besides, I think I should like to go home.

GLINDA: All you have to do is knock your heels together three times and command the shoes to carry you wherever you wish. They will take you in only three steps, each step made in the wink of an eye.

DOROTHY (*Joyfully*): I shall command them at once. (*Hugs* LION, SCARECROW, *and* TIN WOODMAN) Goodbye, goodbye, everyone. You have all been such good friends, and I will never forget you.

SCARECROW, TIN WOODMAN, LION: Goodbye, Dorothy. We shall always remember you, too. (*Ad lib*)

DOROTHY (*Bows to* GLINDA): I am so grateful for your kindness. (*She stands solemnly and clicks heels together three times.*) Take me home to Aunt Em! (*Blackout, crash of thunder, and curtain quickly closes. Lights come up on apron of stage to reveal* DOROTHY *sitting on the floor, with no shoes on, holding Toto. She stands up, looking dazed.*) Good gracious, here I am in Kansas! (*Points offstage*) And there is Uncle Henry's new farmhouse, and there are the cows in the barnyard. Oh! I've lost the silver shoes. They must have fallen off in the air. (*AUNT EM rushes in and takes* DOROTHY *in her arms.*)

AUNT EM: My darling child! Where in the world have you been?

DOROTHY: In the Land of Oz. (*Gravely*) And here is Toto, too. And, oh, Aunt Em, I'm so glad to be at home again. (*They embrace as curtain falls.*)

The End

How Boots Befooled the King

Adapted from Howard Pyle's *The Wonder Clock*

by Sophie L. Goldsmith

Characters

KING
QUEEN
JESTER
FIRST SUITOR
SECOND SUITOR
HERALD
FATHER
PETER
PAUL
BOOTS
OLD CROCKERY VENDER
HIS DAUGHTER
LORD COUNCILOR
HIS DAUGHTER
COUNCILOR'S FIRST MAIDSERVANT
COUNCILOR'S SECOND MAIDSERVANT
FIRST LADY IN WAITING
SECOND LADY IN WAITING
PRINCESS'S NURSE
PRINCESS

Act I

Scene 1

The throne room of the palace. KING *and* QUEEN *on their thrones, with the* JESTER *at feet of* KING. *Throughout the play, the* JESTER *has barely a speaking part, but acts constantly — dancing, mimicking, talking to his bauble, etc.*

KING: Well, my dear, this has been a quiet day, thank heaven! Not a suitor here for the Princess.

QUEEN [*Going to window*]: Not so fast, Husband! The road is crowded. At this very moment, a young man is knocking at the door, and others are jostling him hard.

KING: A plague on them! Will they leave me no peace?

QUEEN: Now, now, dear, keep cool! I'm sure I can't help it if she's so attractive, although [*simpering*] in a way it *is* my fault.

KING: No, no, I won't have you reproach yourself! It is my fault that she is so irresistible — all mine.

QUEEN: No, my love, *I* insist on taking the blame.

KING: Well, well, we'll try not to quarrel. [*Flourish of trumpet. Enter* HERALD.]

HERALD: Your Majesty, the Prince of Thingumbobbia solicits an audience with you.

KING: Show him in. [HERALD *brings in* FIRST SUITOR.]

FIRST SUITOR: O, King, I have come to pay court to your daughter.

KING: Sing it again.

FIRST SUITOR: I said, I have come to pay court to your daughter. There is none like her, so goes the rumor, throughout the length and breadth of the land. I would have her for my bride.

QUEEN: And what have you done, to deserve such a treasure?

FIRST SUITOR: The six-headed dragon have I slain, O King!

KING: Proceed.

FIRST SUITOR: Also, I possess the cap of invisibility and the magic ring.

QUEEN: I implore you, King, do not listen to him! The house is already overrun with caps and rings, which are picturesque, but powerless.

KING [*Patting her hand reassuringly*]: Fear not, little one. [*To* FIRST SUITOR] You do not interest me, sir. I already have a patent dragon-killer, and, as the Queen says, in the way of invisible caps and magic rings our interior decorations are complete.

FIRST SUITOR: But —

KING: Good day, sir!

FIRST SUITOR: Just allow me, sire —

KING: Away with you! [JESTER *ushers him out, mockingly.*]

QUEEN: I think you might be just a little bit gentler, dear.

KING: Pah! Must they be treated like women? If the Princess had been a man, I'd have been saved all this trouble, anyhow.

QUEEN: Are you again blaming me for that? Oh dear! oh dear! [*Starts to weep*]

KING: There, there, my dear, don't take it so hard. You did your best, I know. [*Another knock*] Is that another suitor? [*Enter* HERALD]

HERALD: The Duke of Woddyecallem to see Your Majesty.

QUEEN [*Drying her eyes*]: Show him in. [HERALD *ushers in* SECOND SUITOR.]

SECOND SUITOR: Good day, Your Majesty!

KING [*Impatiently*]: Well, well, well!

SECOND SUITOR: I have come —

KING: Yes, yes, be quick!

SECOND SUITOR: To ask your permission —

KING: Another one! Good heavens!

SECOND SUITOR: But do allow me to finish, Your Majesty! I only want leave to marry your lovely daughter.

QUEEN: *Only,* sir, *only!* You have a strange way of putting it.

SECOND SUITOR: That is true, madam. But see what I have to offer her!

KING: Well, what have you to offer her?

SECOND SUITOR [*Drawing near, confidentially*]: I have a magic horse which, if I but say Gurrumgorrroooo, will carry me wherever I wish.

QUEEN: I don't like that. I want my son-in-law to be a home-loving man.

KING: What else have you?

SECOND SUITOR: I have a magic sword which kills all who fight against it.

KING: That's not a sporting proposition. I like to see a good scrap. What else have you?

SECOND SUITOR: I have a loaf of bread which never grows smaller. As soon as a piece is bitten off, there is another in its place.

QUEEN: Send him away, Your Majesty, send him away! Our daughter is quite lazy enough already! Why shouldn't she bake bread every day, I'd like to know?

KING: Yes, indeed! What else is the poor girl to do? Away with you, Duke Woddyecallem!

SECOND SUITOR: But —

KING: Away, I say! [DUKE *kneels.* JESTER *drives him out.*]

QUEEN: Well, I'm glad that's over. Magic loaf, indeed! Why, the Princess would certainly do nothing *but* loaf! Ha! Ha!

KING: It's all very well for you to joke and make bad puns, but I have no peace any more. These fellows will be the death of me.

QUEEN: My poor kingy-wingy!

KING: I tell you I am weary of it all! A pack of braggarts and impostors! None of them can fool *me!*

JESTER: Would you have one who *could* fool you, sire? Why not try me?

KING [*Gazes at him intently. Rises, strikes his forehead dramatically with his scepter*]: Not so bad, fool, not so bad! [JESTER *begins to hum Wedding March, walking to altar, etc.*]

QUEEN: My liege! Not that person?

KING: Nonsense! Have I not listened to his fooleries these many years, without being taken in by them? [JESTER *collapses in mock despair.*] Herald! Come hither!

HERALD: I am hither, sire!

KING: Proclaim far and wide that only the man who can befool the King shall win his daughter. Those who fail shall be soundly beaten!

QUEEN: But, sire, have mercy! You, who are so penetrating, so wise, who can fool you?

KING: Proclaim it, Herald! Only the man who can befool the wisest King in the world may marry his daughter! Those who fail shall be soundly beaten!

QUEEN: Alas! Alas! She will die an old maid!

KING: Be still, woman! Herald, proclaim!

HERALD: Oyez! Oyez! Oyez! His Gracious Majesty King Wiseacres proclaims that only the man who can befool him shall marry the lovely Princess! Those who fail shall be soundly beaten! [*Walking to other side of stage.*] Oyez! Oyez! Oyez! His Gracious Majesty King Wisacres proclaims that only the man who can befool him shall marry the lovely Princess! Those who fail shall be soundly beaten! [QUEEN *falls at feet of* KING, *begging for mercy.*]

Curtain

Act II

Scene 1

FATHER, PETER, PAUL, *and* BOOTS *seated in their cottage, in front of a fireplace.* PETER *whittling,* PAUL *idle,* BOOTS *poking in ashes.* FATHER *smoking long pipe.*

FATHER: Did you hear the King's proclamation, boys?

PETER: Aye, that we did! And we mean to have a try for the Princess.

FATHER: Go, by all means. It would be fine to have a princess in the family.

PETER: I try first, for I am the oldest.

PAUL: And if he fails, I shall try my luck.

FATHER: Yes, indeed! For one of you two must surely be able to befool the King, fine fellows that you are.

BOOTS: And if they fail, how about me?

PETER: You? *You?* But that is too droll! A stupid fellow like you!

PAUL: You, who do naught all day but poke in the ashes!

BOOTS: That's as it may be. If you fail, may I not have my turn?

FATHER: *If* they fail! Ha! Ha! That's a safe promise! Do you think you can succeed where they fail?

BOOTS: But I may try?

FATHER: Yes, you may try. And now hurry, get your brothers ready.

PETER: Hand me my plumed cap, stupid! So you think I go courting bareheaded?

PAUL: Don't you see I am waiting for my staff, idiot? And a handkerchief to dust off my shoes. Am I to appear before the Princess with dirty shoes?

BOOTS [*Bustling about as required*]: Yes, yes, dear brothers. Go, and good luck to you!

FATHER: Good luck! Good luck!

PETER: And you shall have your chance, Boots, if we fail!

PAUL: Yes, *if* we fail! Ha! Ha!

BOTH: Ha! Ha! [*Go out laughing,* BOOTS *and* FATHER *waving good-by*]

Curtain

79

Scene 2

Same as Act I. KING, QUEEN, *and* JESTER *in throne room. Enter* HERALD.

HERALD: A suitor for the Princess, Your Majesty.

KING: Does he look promising?

HERALD: I cannot tell, Your Majesty. His name is Peter.

QUEEN: Peter! Peter! Rhymes with wife-beater. The sound of it likes me not!

KING: It sounds healthy to me. Show the fellow in!

HERALD [*Announcing*]: Master Peter! [*Enter* PETER.]

PETER: Good day, Your Majesty. I have come to fool you.

KING: Thanks for the hint.

PETER: Of course, it isn't April Fools' Day, Your Majesty. You will pardon the liberty I take. You proclaimed it yourself.

80

KING: What an idiot! And you think *you* can fool *me!*

PETER: Yes, yes, Your Majesty. I know I can. Only look outside in the courtyard.

KING: Yes.

PETER: Do you not see? There are three black geese there. Ha! Ha! Ha! Three black geese, I said!

KING: I see only one goose right in this room, and in a moment he will be not only black, but black and blue. Off with you! [JESTER *beats him out of the room with a small switch.*]

KING: Well, that's one, so far. Fool me indeed! *Me!*

HERALD: Another suitor for the Princess, Your Highness.

KING: What is his name?

HERALD: It is Paul, Your Majesty.

KING: Paul? Rhymes with fall. He'd better not come in.

QUEEN: Ah, give him a chance, Your Majesty. Suppose my father had treated you that way!

KING: True, true. Show him in.

HERALD [*Ushering in* PAUL]: Enter, Paul.

PAUL: Good morrow, Your Majesty.

KING: Well, sirrah?

PAUL: My brother has just left here. A clumsy lout.

KING: Ah, your brother? Same family? [JESTER *starts testing his switch.*]

PAUL: He thought he could fool you. Now I am not so vain.

KING: No?

PAUL: No. Of course I want to marry the Princess, and that is why I'm here.

KING: Yes? [QUEEN *yawns.*]

PAUL: Yes, I know I can't fool *you*. But look — only look out of the window, sire!

KING: Your brother wanted me to look in the courtyard.

PAUL: No, the window! The window!

KING: What for?

PAUL: Do you not see? There is a crow sitting in that tree, and he has three white stripes on his back. Ha! Ha! I fooled you that time!

KING: A crow with three white stripes, did you say?

PAUL: Yes, yes, three white stripes.

KING: Well, I see a donkey in here who will soon have more stripes than three on his back. Take that, and that, and that! [JESTER *administers punishment with zest.*]

PAUL: Ow! Ow! Ow!

KING: And that!

[JESTER *gives final touch as* PAUL *runs from room.* KING *drops exhausted on his throne.* QUEEN *fans him.* JESTER *lovingly fingers switch.*]

Curtain

Scene 3

A quiet street near the palace. In one corner is a booth behind which stands the old CROCKERY VENDER *and her* DAUGHTER. *China, pots and pans, etc., in booth.*

CROCKERY VENDER: Business has been very bad today.

DAUGHTER: Yes, indeed! No one seems to want china dishes. Why don't you sell ribbons and laces?

CROCKERY VENDER: You think of nothing but vanity. Ribbons and laces, indeed! And how would you eat were it not for cups and dishes?

DAUGHTER: I would rather wear pretty things than eat, any day. Then perhaps a king's son would see me and love me.

CROCKERY VENDER: King's son, indeed! [BOOTS *comes strolling along in his old, ragged clothes.*] Here comes one who is more for the likes of you!

DAUGHTER: What! That shabby fellow!

CROCKERY VENDER: Who knows? Clothes are not everything.

BOOTS [*Approaching*]: Good morrow, mother.

DAUGHTER: Mother, indeed! Not so fast, young man!

83

CROCKERY VENDER: Will you be quiet, foolish girl?

BOOTS: That was only in jest, young lady, I assure you.

DAUGHTER: I should hope so! Presumptuous puppy!

CROCKERY VENDER: Will you be wanting any pots or crocks, sir? I have the very finest.

BOOTS: How much will you take for the whole lot?

CROCKERY VENDER: The whole lot?

DAUGHTER: He is mad! Name a high price!

CROCKERY VENDER: Three shillings, young sir. Not a penny less.

DAUGHTER: Three shillings! Not a penny less!

BOOTS: Very well. But you must do exactly as I say.

CROCKERY VENDER: Oh yes, sir, yes sir, anything!

BOOTS: Come here and I will tell you.

DAUGHTER: Take his money first.

BOOTS: Done! Here it is, dame. [*Counting*] One, two, three. But your daughter may not share our secret.

DAUGHTER:
    'Tis little I care.
    I'm off to the Fair,
    To buy me fine laces and bows for my hair.
    Good-by, good-by! [*Exit* DAUGHTER, *dancing off stage*]

BOOTS [*To* CROCKERY VENDER]: Will you do exactly as I say?

CROCKERY VENDER: Yes, yes! [BOOTS *whispers to old* CROCKERY VENDER.]

Curtain

Scene 4

Same as Scene 3. Old CROCKERY VENDER *with her wares at extreme end of stage as* BOOTS *enters from other end, waving away an imaginary crowd.*

BOOTS: No, I will not! I will not do it, I say! Stop pestering me! Go away! I will *not!*

KING [*Entering with* QUEEN]: Who is this, making such an uproar near my palace?

BOOTS: Sorry, Your Majesty, but I am trying to run away from all the people who are pestering me.

KING: Why should they pester you?

BOOTS: They all want to buy my cap, and I don't want to sell it.

KING: But why should anyone want to buy such a cap as that?

BOOTS: Because it is a fooling cap, the only one in all the world.

KING: A fooling cap? I should like to see you fool someone with it. [*Looking around in search of someone.*] Could you fool that old body yonder, with the pots and crocks?

BOOTS: Oh yes, that is easily done. How do you want me to fool her?

KING: Make her break all her pots and pans.

QUEEN: Your Majesty! That poor old soul!

KING: Tush, madam! 'Tis but a jest! A fooling cap indeed!

BOOTS: I assure Your Majesty I have but to blow in the cap and it will obey my every command.

85

KING: Blow away, then!

BOOTS [*Takes off his cap very elaborately and carefully, making many passes with it. Then he blows into it, solemnly, and as he finishes, calls out*]: Now break pots! Break pots! [*Old* CROCKERY VENDER *immediately jumps up and begins breaking one pot after another.*]

KING: Upon my soul!

QUEEN: You had best buy the cap from the fellow, or he will fool the Princess away from us for sure and certain!

KING: Do you think I need you to tell me that? There is not a moment to be lost. Come, fellow, sell me the hat.

BOOTS: No, indeed! Sell my precious fooling cap? No, indeed!

KING: Come, come — if I give you a purse of gold?

BOOTS: No, no!

KING: Two purses of gold?

BOOTS: No, no! My precious cap!

KING: A whole bag of gold?

BOOTS: We-e-ell, perhaps —

KING: Quick, Herald, a bag of gold! [HERALD *brings a bag of gold.* KING *throws it to* BOOTS. BOOTS *gives cap to* KING. KING *takes cap and blows in it. To* QUEEN *as he puts the cap on and places his crown on* BOOTS' *head.*] My dear, who is King now — this fellow or myself?

QUEEN: Ah, no cap can fool me, sire. It is you [*curtsying*] who are King.

KING [*Hastily taking his crown again, and dusting it off*]: H'm! It is but natural that my royalty should be so evident. Still, I am a bit disappointed. Let me think. [*Reflects*] What ho, Page!

PAGE: Your Highness?

KING: Fetch me a lemon, Page! [PAGE *exits and returns at once with a lemon.*] Now taste it, Page.

PAGE: Must I, Your Majesty?

KING: By royal command. But wait! [*He blows long and solemnly into his cap.*] Now taste it. Is it not delicious?

PAGE [*Tastes lemon and makes wry face*]: Your Majesty, it is sour as a lemon.

KING [*Blowing into cap again*]: Take another taste, Page!

PAGE [*On his knees*]: Mercy, Your Majesty!

KING: Nonsense! You will find it so sweet it will positively cloy!

PAGE [*Tasting it again with reluctance and with still wryer face*]: No more, Your Majesty, I implore!

KING: What! Is it possible that *I* have been fooled?

BOOTS: I fear so, my liege. And now, may I marry the Princess?

KING: Not so fast, not so fast! To be sure, you fooled me, but not enough. Still, I will give you another chance, for you are a clever fellow.

BOOTS: What is my task?

QUEEN: Perhaps I can give you an idea, my lord.

KING: Let us hear it.

QUEEN: There is the Lord High Councilor, who is, next to you, the wisest man in all the world. Could you fool him?

BOOTS: It might be done.

QUEEN: Very well, then. If you can fool the Lord High Councilor so as to bring him to the castle tomorrow morning against his will, the Princess is yours.

BOOTS: I shall try, Your Majesty.

KING: Remember, he is to come against his will.

BOOTS: I shall remember, Your Royal Highness.

[*Exit* KING, QUEEN *and* HERALD. BOOTS *and old* CROCKERY VENDER *dance around joyously together.*]

Curtain

Act III

Scene 1

A *room in the* LORD HIGH COUNCILOR's *house.* COUNCILOR *seated,* DAUGHTER *standing next to him. Enter* FIRST SERVANT.

FIRST SERVANT: Lord High Councilor!

LORD HIGH COUNCILOR: What is it?

FIRST SERVANT: Have you heard the news, Lord High Councilor?

LORD HIGH COUNCILOR: No. What is it?

FIRST SERVANT: The King has said that if Boots can bring you to the castle against your will, he may marry the Princess.

DAUGHTER: As though anyone could do that, Father! Are you not the wisest man in all the world?

LORD HIGH COUNCILOR: So I've been told.

DAUGHTER: And the cleverest?

LORD HIGH COUNCILOR: *I* think so.

DAUGHTER: Well, then! [*To* SERVANT] Silly thing, how can he be brought to the castle against his will?

FIRST SERVANT: But, mistress, it is not *I* who say so. Such is the King's proclamation.

DAUGHTER: Foolish girl! Do not let me hear any such nonsense! No one can fool my *father!* [*Enter* SECOND SERVANT]

SECOND SERVANT: Master! Master!

LORD HIGH COUNCILOR: What now?

SECOND SERVANT: Master, there is something strange outside the door.

DAUGHTER: Strange? What does it look like?

SECOND SERVANT: It is a great meal sack, mistress, and somebody lying in it.

DAUGHTER: What nonsense!

SECOND SERVANT: But I assure you it is true! And all this person say as he lies in the sack is "*Sh! Sh! Sh!*"

LORD HIGH COUNCILOR: Strange — very strange! I must go and see it!

DAUGHTER: Do not go, Father! There may be danger!

LORD HIGH COUNCILOR: Very well, then, you bring the sack in here.

DAUGHTER: How wise you are, dearest Father! [*To* SERVANTS] Go then. Don't stand gaping there!

FIRST SERVANT: But suppose he does not wish to come?

SECOND SERVANT: Yes, suppose there should be danger for *us!*

LORD HIGH COUNCILOR: Go at once, cowards that you are!

[*Exit* SERVANTS, *timidly. They return, dragging the meal sack, one at each end. In the sack lies* BOOTS. *They put the sack down between the* COUNCILOR *and his* DAUGHTER.]

LORD HIGH COUNCILOR: This is indeed strange! How came you here?

BOOTS: *Sh! Sh! Sh!*

DAUGHTER: What is your business here, strange fellow?

BOOTS: *Sh! Sh!* I am not to be talked to now. This is a wisdom sack, and I am learning wisdom as fast as a drake can eat peas.

LORD HIGH COUNCILOR: What wisdom have you learned, for example?

BOOTS: Well, I have learned that the clever fellow who fooled the King yesterday is coming with seventeen tall men to take you to the castle, whether you want to, or not.

LORD HIGH COUNCILOR [*Trembling*]: And have you learned how I can get the better of this clever rogue?

BOOTS: Oh, yes, I have learned that easily enough.

LORD HIGH COUNCILOR: Oh, wise man! If you will tell me, I will give you twenty pounds.

BOOTS: No, no! Wisdom is not bought as cheaply as that!

LORD HIGH COUNCILOR: One hundred pounds, then?

BOOTS: That's better. If you will give me one hundred pounds, you may get into the sack yourself and learn all the wisdom you want, and more besides.

LORD HIGH COUNCILOR: Oh, thank you, learned man! Here are your one hundred pounds!

BOOTS: Let me help you into the sack.

[*Helps him in. Gets him comfortably settled, very ostentatiously, then suddenly pulls the string and starts off for the palace.*]

LORD HIGH COUNCILOR [*Calling and struggling*]: Help! Help! Help!

BOOTS: Call all you want, Lord Councilor! I have you safe in my bag and to the palace you go against your will. For I must and shall marry the Princess!

[*Exit* BOOTS, *dragging the* COUNCILOR, *in the sack, after him.* DAUGHTER *and* MAIDS *stand with upraised hands and open mouths, looking after them.*]

Curtain

Scene 2

KING, QUEEN, *and* JESTER *in the throne room* [*same as Act I*]. *Enter* BOOTS, *drawing after him the* COUNCILOR, *still kicking and struggling in the sack.*

BOOTS: Your Majesty, I have come to marry the Princess. Here is the Councilor, and I think it is plain that he is here against his will. [*More kicks from the* COUN-CILOR]

KING: Yes, I think that is reasonably plain.

BOOTS: Will you introduce me to the Princess, please?

KING: Ah, that is another matter. Royalty is not so hasty in these affairs.

QUEEN: No, indeed, our daughter is not so easily won.

KING: Why, you do not even know her! And *that* gives me an idea!

QUEEN: My clever, clever King!

KING: Thank you, my love. I deserve it, but still, thank you.

BOOTS: Do you mean there is still another task for me?

KING: Why, yes, I do! And this time it will not be so easily accomplished.

BOOTS: Speak, I beg you!

KING: If you will come tomorrow morning, you may have the Princess and welcome. *But —*

BOOTS: Yes, yes?

KING: But you must pick her out from among her maidens, who will be dressed just as she is.

QUEEN: Wonderful, Your Majesty, wonderful! The Princess is saved from this adventurer. He can never do it.

BOOTS: I shall try, Your Royal Highness. But this time you will surely give me the Princess?

KING: On my honor as a king, sir!

BOOTS: Your hand on that, Your Royal Highness.

KING: My hand, Mr. Boots! [*They shake hands.*]

Curtain

Scene 3

QUEEN *and* NURSE *sit surrounded by maidens, all dressed exactly alike, in white capes [covering their previous costumes, if necessary], collars of ermine and bandeaux of same.*

QUEEN: I declare, I am the Princess's mother, and it is hard for me to tell which of them all she is!

NURSE: Hush! Hush! At any moment the young man may come in. We must not give away the secret!

QUEEN: You must be most careful, Nurse. You know, as the Princess's nurse, you are the most likely to say something to her, or go over and pet her.

NURSE: I? Indeed I would do no such thing! Would I? [*Running over to* PRINCESS *and arranging her bandeau.*] Now would I, dear Princess? I wouldn't talk to you for all the world.

FIRST LADY IN WAITING: What are you doing now, silly? Quick! The young man may be peeking even now.

SECOND LADY IN WAITING: Yes, they say he is so clever he can see through a wall and hear through any door.

NURSE: You be careful, my darling, if you marry a man like that!

FIRST LADY IN WAITING: Will you stop talking to her, Nurse! I declare, you're giving me the fidgets! Can't we do something to while away the time?

QUEEN: Why don't you dance, ladies? The new steps that the dancing master taught you last week.

SECOND LADY IN WAITING: Very well, madam. Take your places, everyone!

[*Dance. Melody suggested, Edward German's Morris Dances.*]

NURSE: See, here comes the King. And he has with him the Lord High Councilor and a strange man. [*Turning toward the* PRINCESS] Oh, I do hope he is a *nice* young man, my darling!

QUEEN: Will you be quiet, or must I send you from the room?

KING [*Entering with* BOOTS *and* COUNCILOR]: Here is the Princess, among the maidens. See if you can find her.

LORD HIGH COUNCILOR: Yes, see if you can find her, clever one!

[Boots *takes from his pocket a box. He opens it, and out of it there jumps a mouse. A mechanical toy may be used for this purpose; or, failing that, a stuffed cotton mouse, on elastic bands to make it snap from its box, will suit the purpose. There is great confusion among the girls, who scream, run, and jump on chairs. One of them faints away in the middle of the stage. When the others see this, they run to her, chafe her hands, fan her, bring her water, etc.*]

Boots [*Pointing to her as she rises*]: *That* is the Princess!

King: You are right, young man. I see there is no fooling you. Take her — she is yours!

Curtain

The End

A Spider Spectacular

A Radio Play

by Rod Coneybeare

Characters

NARRATOR
MALE SPIDER
FEMALE SPIDER
FLY
INSECT

NARRATOR: It's a lovely summer afternoon. The trees overhang the stream. There's hardly a wind stirring. The sun is a warm blanket. There's a fallen log jutting out of the stream at one point and close beside, a blackberry bush. Between these two is strung a spider web. Let's look closer . . . and closer, until the web is as big to our eyes as it is to the spider.

Now it looks like a fantastic maze of ropes. Way up at the top, working on the ropes, a very large spider. Down in the corner, on the ground by the bush is a much smaller spider.

MALE SPIDER: Slllurp. Arh. Ahhh. Well, there's the last of that fly. Aheh, heh. That last fly had a much better taste, didn't it, honey? Honey? Honey, did you hear me?

FEMALE (*From a distance*): Shut up, I'm busy. I'm sick of you.

MALE: Aw. She never talks to me. Always repairing the web. Talk about a one-track mind. Hee, ha, ha! I know. Hee, ha, ha! I'll pull the telephone wire. That'll wake her up. I'll just reach over and. . . .

SOUND (*Like a piano string being plucked and then breaking*): Twaaaannnggggggggggggg.

MALE: Ha, ha, ha. Ah ha, ha, ha. Oh boy, did you jump! Ha, ha. You thought you caught another fly, didn't you, honey? Ah ha, ha, ha, ha. Ah ha, ha.

FEMALE: All right! Another one of your silly pranks, eh? I've had enough.

MALE: Oh, aw honey, I — was just playing games.

FEMALE: I should have eaten you long ago.

MALE: Ohhh.

FEMALE: Most females of my species eat their husbands as soon as the children are on the way. You're a lazy, good-for-nothing lump, like all male spiders.

MALE: Awww.

FEMALE: You don't even spin webs. Not only that, you sit here eating the food I catch while I'm busy putting the stickum on the web to trap the flies. I've been soft letting you live.

MALE: Aw, now honey. . . .

FEMALE: I mean it!

MALE (*To himself*): Oh, boy. She *does* mean it. And she's three times my size. I can't argue with her. Those great big fangs could paralyze me in a minute. I've got to think fast. I've got to. . . . (*Out loud*) Watch out behind you!

FEMALE: Why? Why?

SOUND: (*Footsteps going off*)

FEMALE: Hmmmm. How silly of me to fall for that. There's nothing in this world I haven't been able to overpower. I suppose I should follow him and truss him up with my silk and keep him in case there's a food shortage. Uh. Never mind. He's such a puny thing I can't be bothered. Besides, if I ever get really hungry, I can always eat the children.

SOUND: (*Twangy footsteps as the spider climbs up the web*)

FEMALE: I guess I'd better climb up and continue putting the glue on the line.

SOUND (*A fly buzzes close and away.*): BBBzzzzzzzzzzzz.

FEMALE: Huh.

SOUND: Bzzzzzzzzz.

FEMALE: Ah. You almost got caught. A nice juicy fly, too. Just missed the web. Oh, well. There should be plenty of flies come by on a day like this.

SOUND (*Like a can of oil being squeezed*): Clug-gug, clug-gug.

FEMALE: Ahhh. I've been eating so well that I'm full of all kinds of glue. I should have the web covered with nice sticky glue very soon. There should be something nice and juicy along pretty soon.

FLY: Bzzzzzz. Da, da, doobebe, da da. Ah, it's a pretty nice day. Hot though. Oh boy, you can't get up much speed. I weigh too much after all that delicious chocolate cake I ate last night, I guess. Aha. Doodoodedoo. Hey, there's a nice stream down there. Maybe I'll fly down to see if it's a bit cooler. Oh deedee. Oh, I am a green-bottle fly. There's no fly greener than I. I am a green-bottle fly. I, oh, ya, oh, what's this.

SOUND (*Fly getting tangled in the web*): Twanggyzumbum.

FLY: Oh, ah, hey, where am I? Yechhh, yecchh, I can't get my wings going. I'm stuck in something. I can't lift my leg. Ah, it sticks like glue. I've got to get out, I've got to. Uhhhhhh!

FEMALE: Good afternoon.

FLY: Oh, what is it? It's horrible, a horrible creature.

FEMALE: You didn't watch where you were going, did you?

FLY: What — what are you going to do?

FEMALE: I'm going to wrap you up, nice and warm, Mr. Green-bottle.

SOUND (*Water in the brook gurgles.*)

FEMALE: Mmmmm, he was a good meal, nice and plump. I suppose I should have just left him wrapped in silk and just stuck him with my fangs and put him aside for a rainy day. I really do have a tendency to overeat. My stomach is huge. I can hardly move. Well, I'll just sit here at the edge of the web by the telephone line. If anything else gets caught, the telephone line will jiggle and let me know because it's attached to the center of the web. Ohhhh, uhmmm. It's nice to be an *Aranea diadema* spider. Mmmmm. I imagine I'm about the deadliest creature in the world. There doesn't seem to be anything I can't just truss up, paralyze, and drain blood from.

SOUND (*Something strikes the web.*): Plunnnnggggg!

FEMALE: Oh, my. Whatever that is must be huge. It must be huge. I'll hurry up the web. Maybe it's a nice juicy grasshopper. Now let me think. With grasshoppers I usually first give them a bite in the leg.

SOUND (*Roaring, like an airplane engine*): Rrrrrrrrrrrr.

FEMALE: What is it? I've never seen anything like this before.

INSECT: Hello, there, dearie.

FEMALE: Hello.

INSECT: You've got a lovely web here.

FEMALE: Thank you.

INSECT: Looks like I'm caught, doesn't it?

FEMALE: Yes, it does.

INSECT: Well. *C'est la vie.*

FEMALE: What?

INSECT: That means, "that's life," or words to that effect. Ha, ha.

FEMALE: Oh, what are you?

INSECT: Oh, just a poor insect that's about to meet its doom, I guess. Huh. Oh well, we've all got to go sometime.

FEMALE: You've got pretty strong wings. I think if you buzzed a bit more, you'd tear my web and escape.

INSECT: Oh, I don't think so. This is such a good web. And it's sticky!

FEMALE: Oh?

INSECT: Say, you must be an *Aranea diadema* to have such glue inside you.

FEMALE: Yes, I am.

INSECT: Well, don't prolong it, honey. Give me the old stinger and let me rest in peace.

FEMALE: You're a female.

INSECT: Well, sure.

FEMALE: Females are usually the most clever insects.

INSECT: I'll go along with that.

FEMALE: What do you call yourself?

INSECT: Oh, nothing in particular. Say, you know you're going to have to get closer if you want to paralyze me, aren't you?

FEMALE: You don't seem worried.

INSECT: Oh, maybe I'm tired of life, uh, huh.

FEMALE: Well, well if that's what you want.

INSECT: Oh, that's what I want, honey. Just give me the old fangs. I'm sick of this world. I don't care what happens to me. Say, those are lovely fangs you have. That's right. Closer, closer, closer.

SOUND: Bzzzzzzzzzzzzz.

FEMALE: Ohhohoh. What are you? What are you?

INSECT: A Mud-dobber Wasp, dearie. And this time you're the one who gets paralyzed. Hee, hee! I'll just put you into one of the nice cozy cells in my nest. And when the eggs in the cell hatch, they'll have a delicious spider to eat to keep them alive. Hmm. Oh, boy, you are heavy. Nice and fat. Well, let's go.

SOUND (*Roaring like engines of a plane*): Rrrrrrrrrrr. (*Then, sound of brook and birds*)

NARRATOR: It's a typical summer day, drowsy, nothing much happening. A boy walks along, his hands in his pockets, not thinking about very much. He walks between the log and the bush and breaks the cobweb. Some of it clings to his trousers. He doesn't even notice.

The End

Further Reading

Act It Out by Bernice Carlson
The Bag of Fire and Other Plays by Fan Kissen
The Crowded House and Other Plays by Fan Kissen
Entrances and Exits by Phyllis Fenner and Avah Hughes
Fifty Plays for Junior Actors by Sylvia Kamerman
First Plays for Children by Helen Louise Miller
Folk Plays for Puppets by Tom Tichenor
How to Have a Show by Barbara Beck
It's Time to Give a Play
    by Janet Woolsey and Elizabeth Sechrist
Pantomimes, Charades, and Skits by Vernon Howard
A Play at Your House by Regina Brown
Plays and How to Put Them On by Moyne Rice Smith
The Scarlet Thread by Mary Hays Weik
The Straw Ox and Other Plays by Fan Kissen
They Helped Make America by Fan Kissen

Next, see "Stage a Play" and "You're on the Air" in DOING; "Doing Pantomime," "Story Theater," "Making a Play," and "Be an Actor" in ACTING OUT.

Plays on circled ○ pages have been recorded. Look for them under *Short Plays* 1 in the LISTENING LIBRARY.

Art Credits

The King's Bean Soup illustrated by Brian Froud
The Heroic Vegetables illustrated by Marc Brown
African Trio illustrated by Jerry Pinkney
Wizard of Oz, still #1060-50, 132, 133, 8, 206. © 1939,
Metro-Goldwyn-Mayer Inc.
How Boots Befooled the King illustrated by **John Freas**
A Spider Spectacular, photographs by Ann Moreton
Cover photographs by David Robbins

BCDEFGHIJ·B·78210987 6 5 4 3